Everyday Mathematics®

The University of Chicago School Mathematics Project

Skills Link

Teacher's Guide
Cumulative Practice Sets

 Grade 4

Mc Graw Hill **Wright Group**

The McGraw·Hill Companies

www.WrightGroup.com

 **Wright Group**

Contents

Introduction to *Skills Link*

Welcome to *Skills Link*, a cumulative practice supplement to *Everyday Mathematics* for Grades 1–6. *Skills Link* is a valuable resource for providing additional practice in your classroom.

The Grade 4 *Skills Link* book is composed of three sections: Grade 3 Review, Grade 4 Practice Sets, and Grade 4 Test Practice. Each of these sections is designed to reinforce the skills and concepts covered in the Grade 4 *Everyday Mathematics* program by providing additional practice in a variety of formats. (See pages 3–5 for more information on these sections.)

Grade 3 Review

This section provides a review of material from *Everyday Mathematics* Grade 3. The problems are organized by content strand, and are intended to be assigned early in the school year to ascertain students' retention of *Everyday Mathematics* Grade 3 Grade-Level Goals.

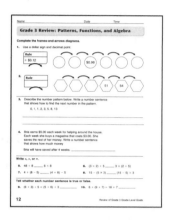

Practice Sets

There are 93 Practice Sets in Grade 4, allowing approximately seven to nine Practice Sets per unit. Each Practice Set is cumulative; the content is covered during or prior to the *Everyday Mathematics* lesson referenced on the Practice Set page. This way, you can be sure your students will be practicing skills they have already been taught.

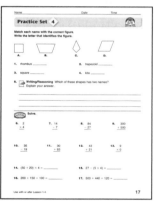

Test Practice

The final section of Grade 4 *Skills Link* provides an opportunity for students to practice mathematics skills in a multiple-choice, standardized test format. Each Test Practice set covers two or three units of material. The footer at the bottom of each Test Practice page indicates when the Test Practice set should be assigned.

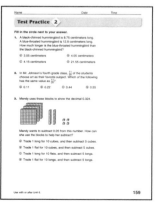

Features of the *Skills Link* Student Book include

◆ Facts Practice and Computation Practice problem sets that promote automaticity with basic facts and operations

◆ Writing/Reasoning problems that encourage students to explain their problem-solving strategies using words, numbers, and pictures

◆ References to pages in the *Student Reference* Book where more information about the topics covered in a Practice Set page may be found. The SRB icon at the top of each Practice Set page lists the most helpful references, but it is not intended to be an exhaustive listing.

◆ Problems that provide practice using multiple strategies, including paper-and-pencil computation, mental computation, and estimation

◆ Models, rules, and examples to facilitate at-home support

◆ Problems that utilize familiar *Everyday Mathematics* routines

Features of the *Skills Link* Teacher's Guide include

◆ Correlation charts that map the content of each *Skills Link* section to *Everyday Mathematics* Grade-Level Goals

◆ An Overview of the Practice Sets that gives you information about which Practice Set can be used with each lesson

◆ Answer Keys for each section of *Skills Link*

Features of Grade 3 Review

Coverage of the Grade 3 Grade-Level Goals, organized by content strand

Name _____ Date _____ Time _____

Grade 3 Review: Patterns, Functions, and Algebra

Complete the frames-and-arrows diagrams.

1. Use a dollar sign and decimal point.

Rule
+ $0.12

◯ ◯ $0.98 ◯ ◯ ◯

Review of familiar *Everyday Math* routines and strategies

2. Rule

⬡ ⬡ ⬡ 51 54 ⬡

3. Describe the number pattern below. Write a number sentence that shows how to find the next number in the pattern.

0, 1, 1, 2, 3, 5, 8, 13

_____

_____

Problems correspond to each goal in the *Everyday Math* content strand.

4. Bria earns $5.00 each week for helping around the house. Each week she buys a magazine that costs $3.00. She saves the rest of her money. Write a number sentence that shows how much money

Bria will have saved after 4 weeks. _____

Write <, >, or =.

5. $48 \div 8$ _____ 6×8

6. $(3 \times 2) + 5$ _____ $3 \times (2 + 5)$

7. $4 + (8 - 5)$ _____ $(4 + 8) - 5$

8. $15 - (5 \times 3)$ _____ $(15 - 5) \times 3$

Tell whether each number sentence is true or false.

9. $(6 + 3) + 5 = (5 + 6) + 3$ _____

10. $6 + (9 + 7) = 16 + 7$ _____

12   Review of Grade 3 Grade-Level Goals

Features of Practice Sets

Each practice set includes a variety of problems.

Student Reference Book pages provide additional information about the content of each practice set.

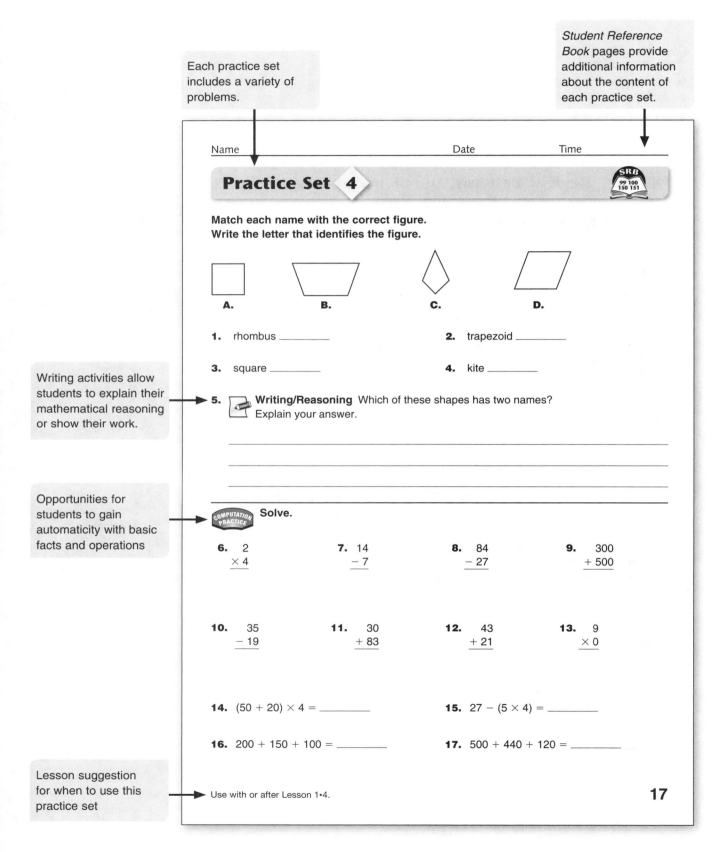

Name _____ Date _____ Time _____

Practice Set 4

SRB
99 100
150 151

Match each name with the correct figure.
Write the letter that identifies the figure.

A.   B.   C.   D.

1. rhombus _____   2. trapezoid _____

3. square _____   4. kite _____

Writing activities allow students to explain their mathematical reasoning or show their work.

5. **Writing/Reasoning** Which of these shapes has two names? Explain your answer.

_____

_____

_____

Opportunities for students to gain automaticity with basic facts and operations

Solve.

6. $\begin{array}{r} 2 \\ \times\ 4 \\ \hline \end{array}$

7. $\begin{array}{r} 14 \\ -\ 7 \\ \hline \end{array}$

8. $\begin{array}{r} 84 \\ -\ 27 \\ \hline \end{array}$

9. $\begin{array}{r} 300 \\ +\ 500 \\ \hline \end{array}$

10. $\begin{array}{r} 35 \\ -\ 19 \\ \hline \end{array}$

11. $\begin{array}{r} 30 \\ +\ 83 \\ \hline \end{array}$

12. $\begin{array}{r} 43 \\ +\ 21 \\ \hline \end{array}$

13. $\begin{array}{r} 9 \\ \times\ 0 \\ \hline \end{array}$

14. $(50 + 20) \times 4 =$ _____   15. $27 - (5 \times 4) =$ _____

16. $200 + 150 + 100 =$ _____   17. $500 + 440 + 120 =$ _____

Lesson suggestion for when to use this practice set

Use with or after Lesson 1·4.   **17**

Features of Test Practice

Variety of problems covering key concepts from Grade 4 units

Name _____ Date _____ Time _____

Test Practice 2

Fill in the circle next to your answer.

1. A black-chinned hummingbird is 8.75 centimeters long. A blue-throated hummingbird is 12.8 centimeters long. How much longer is the blue-throated hummingbird than the black-chinned hummingbird?

   Ⓐ 3.05 centimeters   Ⓑ 4.05 centimeters

   Ⓒ 4.15 centimeters   Ⓓ 21.55 centimeters

2. In Mr. Johnson's fourth grade class, $\frac{11}{20}$ of the students choose art as their favorite subject. Which of the following has the same value as $\frac{11}{20}$?

   Ⓐ 0.11   Ⓑ 0.22   Ⓒ 0.44   Ⓓ 0.55

   Multiple-choice format prepares students for standardized testing

3. Mandy uses these blocks to show the decimal 0.324.

   Mandy wants to subtract 0.05 from this number. How can she use the blocks to help her subtract?

   Ⓐ Trade 1 long for 10 cubes, and then subtract 5 cubes.

   Ⓑ Trade 1 flat for 10 cubes, and then subtract 5 cubes.

   Ⓒ Trade 1 long for 10 flats, and then subtract 5 longs.

   Ⓓ Trade 1 flat for 10 longs, and then subtract 5 longs.

Use with or after Unit 6.

159

Unit suggestion for when to use this test practice

Content	Everyday Mathematics Grade 3 Grade-Level Goals	Grade 3 Skills Review Problems
Number and Numeration		
Place value and notation	**Goal 1.** Read and write whole numbers up to 1,000,000; read, write, and model with manipulatives decimals through hundredths; identify places in such numbers and the values of the digits in those places; translate between whole numbers and decimals represented in words, in base-10 notation, and with manipulatives.	1, 2, 9
Meanings and uses of fractions	**Goal 2.** Read, write, and model fractions; solve problems involving fractional parts of a region or a collection; describe strategies used.	3
Number theory	**Goal 3.** Find multiples of 2, 5, and 10.	4
Equivalent names for whole numbers	**Goal 4.** Use numerical expressions involving one or more of the basic four arithmetic operations to give equivalent names for whole numbers.	5
Equivalent names for fractions, decimals, and percents	**Goal 5.** Use manipulatives and drawings to find and represent equivalent names for fractions; use manipulatives to generate equivalent fractions.	7
Comparing and ordering numbers	**Goal 6.** Compare and order whole numbers up to 1,000,000; use manipulatives to order decimals through hundredths; use area models and benchmark fractions to compare and order fractions.	6, 8
Operations and Computation		
Addition and subtraction facts	**Goal 1.** Demonstrate automaticity with all addition and subtraction facts through 10 + 10; use basic facts to compute fact extensions such as 80 + 70.	13
Addition and subtraction procedures	**Goal 2.** Use manipulatives, mental arithmetic, paper-and-pencil algorithms, and calculators to solve problems involving the addition and subtraction of whole numbers and decimals in a money context; describe the strategies used and explain how they work.	1–4
Multiplication and division facts	**Goal 3.** Demonstrate automaticity with $\times 0$, $\times 1$, $\times 2$, $\times 5$, and $\times 10$ multiplication facts; use strategies to compute remaining facts up to 10×10.	5, 6
Multiplication and division procedures	**Goal 4.** Use arrays, mental arithmetic, paper-and-pencil algorithms, and calculators to solve problems involving the multiplication of 2- and 3-digit whole numbers by 1-digit whole numbers; describe the strategies used.	7–10
Computational estimation	**Goal 5.** Make reasonable estimates for whole number addition and subtraction problems; explain how the estimates were obtained.	11, 12
Models for the operations	**Goal 6.** Recognize and describe change, comparison, and parts-and-total situations; use repeated addition, arrays, and skip counting to model multiplication; use equal sharing and equal grouping to model division.	13

Content	Everyday Mathematics Grade 3 Grade-Level Goals	Grade 3 Skills Review Problems
Data and Chance		
Data collection and representation	**Goal 1.** Collect and organize data or use given data to create charts, tables, bar graphs, and line plots.	1, 2
Data analysis	**Goal 2.** Use graphs to ask and answer simple questions and draw conclusions; find the maximum, minimum, range, mode, and median of a data set.	3–8
Qualitative probability	**Goal 3.** Describe events using *certain, very likely, likely, unlikely, very unlikely, impossible*, and other basic probability terms; explain the choice of language.	9–14
Quantitative probability	**Goal 4.** Predict the outcomes of simple experiments and test the predictions using manipulatives; express the probability of an event by using "___ out of ___" language.	15–20
Measurement and Reference Frames		
Length, weight, and angles	**Goal 1.** Estimate length with and without tools; measure length to the nearest $\frac{1}{2}$ inch and $\frac{1}{2}$ centimeter; draw and describe angles as records of rotations.	1–3
Area, perimeter, volume, and capacity	**Goal 2.** Describe and use strategies to measure the perimeter of polygons; count unit squares to find the areas of rectangles.	4, 5
Units and systems of measurement	**Goal 3.** Describe relationships among inches, feet, and yards; describe relationships between minutes in an hour, hours in a day, days in a week.	6, 7
Time	**Goal 4.** Tell and show time to the nearest minute on an analog clock; tell and write time in digital notation.	8, 9
Geometry		
Lines and angles	**Goal 1.** Identify and draw points, intersecting and parallel line segments and lines, rays, and right angles.	1–3
Plane and solid figures	**Goal 2.** Identify, describe, model, and compare plane and solid figures including circles, polygons, spheres, cylinders, rectangular prisms, pyramids, cones, and cubes using appropriate geometric terms including the terms *face, edge, vertex,* and *base*.	4, 5
Transformations and symmetry	**Goal 3.** Create and complete two-dimensional symmetric shapes or designs; locate multiple lines of symmetry in a two-dimensional shape.	6, 7
Patterns, Functions, and Algebra		
Patterns and functions	**Goal 1.** Extend, describe, and create numeric patterns; describe rules for patterns and use them to solve problems; use words and symbols to describe and write rules for functions involving addition, subtraction, and multiplication and use those rules to solve problems.	1–3
Algebraic notation and solving number sentences	**Goal 2.** Read, write, and explain number sentences using the symbols $+, -, \times, \div, =, >$, and $<$; solve number sentences; write expressions and number sentences to model number stories.	4–8
Order of operations	**Goal 3.** Recognize that numeric expressions can have different values depending on the order in which operations are carried out; understand that grouping symbols can be used to affect the order in which operations are carried out.	9, 10

Grade 3 Review Answer Key

Number and Numeration

1. 0.82

2.

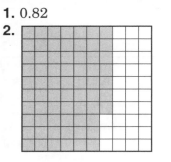

3.

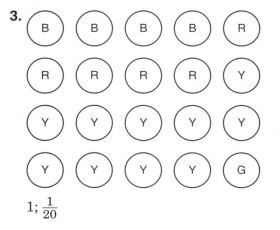

$1; \frac{1}{20}$

4. 5; 10; **15; 20; 25; 30; 35**

5. Answers vary. Sample answer: 10 + 11;
HHT HHT HHT HHT I; ○○○○○○○○○○
○○○○○○○○○○○;
100 −79; 4 × 5 + 1; 42 ÷ 2; 21 × 1;
5 + 5 + 5 + 5 + 1; 30 − 9;

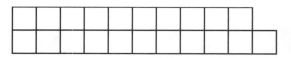

6. a. 7,964 **b.** 35,140 **c.** 861,285 **d.** 604,103

7.

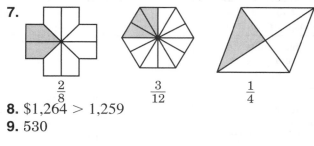

$\frac{2}{8}$ $\frac{3}{12}$ $\frac{1}{4}$

8. $1,264 > 1,259

9. 530

Operations and Computation

1. 90,000 **2.** 60,000 **3.** 20,000

4. 100,000

5. 6 × 9 = 54; 9 × 6 = 54; 54 ÷ 6 = 9;
54 ÷ 9 = 6

6. 7 × 4 = 28; 4 × 7 = 28; 28 ÷ 7 = 4;
28 ÷ 4 = 7

7. 488 **8.** 2,135

9. 504 **10.** 2,520

11. 800 − 400 = 400 **12.** 400 − 100 = 300

13.

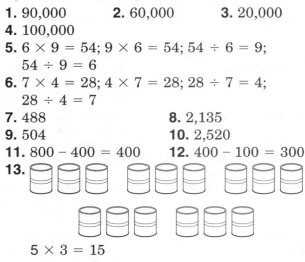

5 × 3 = 15

Data and Chance

1.

Number of Legs on Animals	
Number of Legs	Number of Animals
0	HHT I
2	////
4	///
6	HHT I
8	HHT

2.

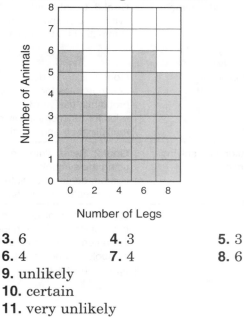

3. 6 **4.** 3 **5.** 3

6. 4 **7.** 4 **8.** 6

9. unlikely

10. certain

11. very unlikely

8 *Skills Link* Teacher's Guide

Data and Chance (cont.)

12. very likely
13. impossible
14. likely
15. 2 out of 12 or 1 out of 6
16. 12 out of 12 or 1 out of 1
17. 9 out of 12 or 3 out of 4
18. 0 out of 12
19. 9 out of 12 or 3 out of 4
20. 6 out of 12 or 1 out of 2

Measurement and Reference Frames

1. $\frac{1}{2}$ turn

2. $\frac{1}{4}$ turn

3. full turn
4. Answers vary. Check students' drawings.
5. Answers vary. Check students' drawings.
6. 3 feet; 11 inches
7. 300 feet
8.

 4:17

9. 12:12 P.M.; 11:15 A.M.

Geometry

1.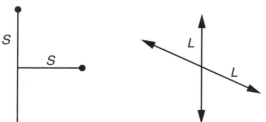

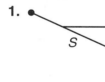

2. 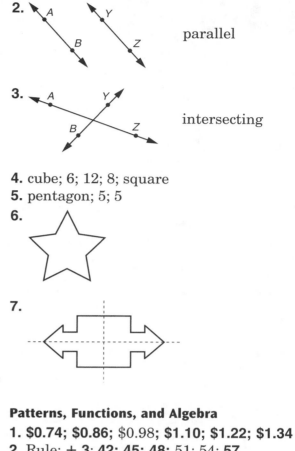 parallel

3. intersecting

4. cube; 6; 12; 8; square
5. pentagon; 5; 5
6.

7.

Patterns, Functions, and Algebra

1. $0.74; $0.86; $0.98; $1.10; $1.22; $1.34
2. Rule: **+ 3**; **42; 45; 48**; 51; 54; **57**
3. Answers vary. Sample answer: Add the two previous numbers together to get the next number. 8 + 13 = 21
4. ($5.00 − $3.00) × 4 = $8.00
5. <   **6.** <
7. =   **8.** <
9. true   **10.** false

Practice Sets Correlated to Grade 4 Goals

Content	Everyday Mathematics Grade 4 Grade-Level Goals	Grade 4 Practice Sets
Number and Numeration		
Place value and notation	**Goal 1.** Read and write whole numbers up to 1,000,000,000 and decimals through thousandths; identify places in such numbers and the values of the digits in those places; translate between whole numbers and decimals represented in words and in base-10 notation.	2, 7, 8, 11, 12, 13, 14, 17, 20, 26, 28, 33, 35, 37, 38, 39, 42, 43, 48, 57, 58, 59, 63, 69, 70, 73, 77, 81
Meanings and uses of fractions	**Goal 2.** Read, write, and model fractions; solve problems involving fractional parts of a region or a collection; describe and explain strategies used; given a fractional part of a region or a collection, identify the unit whole.	17, 21, 22, 25, 32, 40, 48, 51, 53, 54, 58, 63, 67, 68, 69, 72, 73, 79, 80, 82, 85, 89, 91, 92
Number theory	**Goal 3.** Find multiples of whole numbers less than 10; find whole number factors of numbers.	15, 47, 49, 51, 66, 89, 90
Equivalent names for whole numbers	**Goal 4.** Use numerical expressions involving one or more of the basic four arithmetic operations and grouping symbols to give equivalent names for whole numbers.	2, 10, 14, 31, 38, 89, 90
Equivalent names for fractions, decimals, and percents	**Goal 5.** Use numerical expressions to find and represent equivalent names for fractions and decimals; use and explain a multiplication rule to find equivalent fractions; rename fourths, fifths, tenths, and hundredths as decimals and percents.	27, 32, 48, 55, 56, 60, 67, 68, 69, 70, 71, 79, 85, 86, 90
Comparing and ordering numbers	**Goal 6.** Compare and order whole numbers up to 1,000,000,000 and decimals through thousandths; compare and order integers between −100 and 0; use area models, benchmark fractions, and analyses of numerators and denominators to compare and order fractions.	3, 29, 32, 44, 53, 57, 60, 62, 72, 79, 80, 86, 88, 89, 92
Operations and Computation		
Addition and subtraction facts	**Goal 1.** Demonstrate automaticity with basic addition and subtraction facts and fact extensions.	1, 2, 4, 5, 6, 12, 15, 17, 24, 26, 29, 35, 36, 37, 38, 42, 43, 46, 47, 51, 54, 57, 59, 61, 65, 67, 71, 84
Addition and subtraction procedures	**Goal 2.** Use manipulatives, mental arithmetic, paper-and-pencil algorithms, and calculators to solve problems involving the addition and subtraction of whole numbers and decimals through hundredths; describe the strategies used and explain how they work.	2, 4, 11, 12, 15, 17, 19, 23, 24, 26, 27, 28, 30, 31, 33, 34, 37, 40, 41, 42, 43, 44, 47, 51, 54, 57, 69, 71, 72, 77, 80, 84, 87, 89
Multiplication and division facts	**Goal 3.** Demonstrate automaticity with multiplication facts through 10 * 10 and proficiency with related division facts; use basic facts to compute fact extensions such as 30 * 60.	2, 4, 5, 6, 7, 8, 10, 11, 12, 15, 17, 18, 19, 20, 21, 22, 24, 25, 26, 33, 35, 36, 37, 38, 39, 40, 41, 43, 45, 46, 47, 48, 49, 50, 52, 53, 54, 55, 57, 59, 62, 63, 64, 66, 67, 71, 74, 81, 84, 85, 86, 88, 90, 91, 92, 93
Multiplication and division procedures	**Goal 4.** Use mental arithmetic, paper-and-pencil algorithms, and calculators to solve problems involving the multiplication of multidigit whole numbers by 2-digit whole numbers and the division of multidigit whole numbers by 1-digit whole numbers; describe the strategies used and explain how they work.	2, 7, 18, 19, 21, 24, 27, 28, 33, 36, 37, 38, 39, 40, 41, 43, 45, 46, 47, 48, 49, 50, 54, 64, 66, 71, 73, 74, 77, 81, 82, 84, 87, 89, 93

Computational estimation	**Goal 6.** Make reasonable estimates for whole number and decimal addition and subtraction problems, and whole number multiplication and division problems; explain how the estimates were obtained.	9, 15, 23, 29, 37, 38, 39, 43, 48, 52, 66, 85, 93
Models for the operations	**Goal 7.** Use repeated addition, skip counting, arrays, area, and scaling to model multiplication and division.	14, 28, 46, 50, 51, 60

Data and Chance

Data collection and representation	**Goal 1.** Collect and organize data or use given data to create charts, tables, bar graphs, line plots, and line graphs.	21, 29, 36, 41
Data analysis	**Goal 2.** Use the maximum, minimum, range, median, mode, and graphs to ask and answer questions, draw conclusions, and make predictions.	13, 14, 16, 24, 40, 53, 72, 75, 79
Qualitative probability	**Goal 3.** Describe events using *certain, very likely, likely, unlikely, very unlikely, impossible* and other basic probability terms; use *more likely, equally likely, same chance, 50–50, less likely,* and other basic probability terms to compare events; explain the choice of language.	52, 59, 76, 92
Quantitative probability	**Goal 4.** Predict the outcomes of experiments and test the predictions using manipulatives; summarize the results and use them to predict future events; express the probability of an event as a fraction.	18, 36, 52, 59, 76

Measurement and Reference Frames

Length, weight, and angles	**Goal 1.** Estimate length with and without tools; measure length to the nearest $\frac{1}{4}$ inch and $\frac{1}{2}$ centimeter; estimate the size of angles without tools.	16, 30, 33, 35, 49, 50, 74, 75, 77, 86
Area, perimeter, volume, and capacity	**Goal 2.** Describe and use strategies to measure the perimeter and area of polygons, to estimate the area of irregular shapes, and to find the volume of rectangular prisms.	8, 60, 61, 62, 63, 64, 65, 66, 70, 77, 84, 85, 90
Units and systems of measurement	**Goal 3.** Describe relationships among U.S. customary units of length and among metric units of length.	23, 34, 35, 38, 60, 69, 76, 78, 81, 86
Coordinate systems	**Goal 4.** Use ordered pairs of numbers to name, locate, and plot points in the first quadrant of a coordinate grid.	9, 55, 58, 65

Geometry

Lines and angles	**Goal 1.** Identify, draw, and describe points, intersecting and parallel line segments and lines, rays, and right, acute, and obtuse angles.	2, 3, 49, 50, 77, 82
Plane and solid figures	**Goal 2.** Describe, compare, and classify plane and solid figures, including polygons, circles, spheres, cylinders, rectangular prisms, cones, cubes, and pyramids, using appropriate geometric terms including *vertex, base, face, edge,* and *congruent.*	4, 5, 6, 7, 9, 45, 70, 82, 83
Transformations and symmetry	**Goal 3.** Identify, describe, and sketch examples of reflections; identify and describe examples of translations and rotations.	76, 77, 78, 81, 83

Patterns, Functions, and Algebra

Patterns and functions	**Goal 1.** Extend, describe, and create numeric patterns; describe rules for patterns and use them to solve problems; use words and symbols to describe and write rules for functions that involve the four basic arithmetic operations and use those rules to solve problems.	2, 4, 7, 9, 13, 14, 16, 17, 18, 25, 28, 29, 30, 31, 35, 48, 50, 51, 55, 56, 60, 63, 68, 70, 80, 88, 89, 93
Algebraic notation and solving number sentences	**Goal 2.** Use conventional notation to write expressions and number sentences using the four basic arithmetic operations; determine whether number sentences are true or false; solve open sentences and explain the solutions; write expressions and number sentences to model number stories.	5, 24, 25, 26, 27, 32, 33, 38, 39, 45, 51, 52, 58, 64, 69, 73, 77, 78, 89, 92
Order of operations	**Goal 3.** Evaluate numeric expressions containing grouping symbols; insert grouping symbols to make number sentences true.	4, 5, 13, 26, 27, 35, 41, 63, 78, 84
Properties of the arithmetic operations	**Goal 4.** Apply the Distributive Property of Multiplication over Addition to the partial-products multiplication algorithm.	39

Grade 4 Practice Sets Overview

	Practice Set Number	Use with or after This Lesson:	Page Number(s) in Skills Link Student Book
Unit 1	1	1·1	13
	2	1·2	14 and 15
	3	1·3	16
	4	1·4	17 and 18
	5	1·5	19 and 20
	6	1·6	21
	7	1·7	22
	8	1·8	23
Unit 2	9	2·1	24 and 25
	10	2·2	26
	11	2·3	27 and 28
	12	2·4	29
	13	2·5	30 and 31
	14	2·6	32 and 33
	15	2·7	34
	16	2·8	35 and 36
	17	2·9	37 and 38
Unit 3	18	3·1	39
	19	3·2	40 and 41
	20	3·3	42
	21	3·4	43 and 44
	22	3·5	45
	23	3·6	46
	24	3·8	47 and 48
	25	3·9	49
	26	3·10	50
	27	3·11	51 and 52
Unit 4	28	4·1	53 and 54
	29	4·4	55 and 56
	30	4·5	57 and 58
	31	4·6	59
	32	4·7	60
	33	4·8	61 and 62
	34	4·9	63
	35	4·10	64 and 65
Unit 5	36	5·2	66 and 67
	37	5·3	68
	38	5·4	69 and 70
	39	5·5	71
	40	5·6	72 and 73
	41	5·7	74 and 75
	42	5·8	76
	43	5·9	77 and 78
	44	5·11	79

	Practice Set Number	Use with or after This Lesson:	Page Number(s) in Skills Link Student Book
Unit 6	45	6·1	80 and 81
	46	6·2	82 and 83
	47	6·3	84 and 85
	48	6·4	86 and 87
	49	6·6	88
	50	6·8	89 and 90
Unit 7	51	7·2	91 and 92
	52	7·3	93
	53	7·4	94 and 95
	54	7·5	96 and 97
	55	7·7	98 and 99
	56	7·8	100
	57	7·9	101 and 102
	58	7·10	103
	59	7·11	104
Unit 8	60	8·1	105
	61	8·2	106
	62	8·3	107 and 108
	63	8·5	109 and 110
	64	8·6	111
	65	8·7	112 and 113
	66	8·8	114
Unit 9	67	9·1	115 and 116
	68	9·2	117
	69	9·3	118 and 119
	70	9·4	120 and 121
	71	9·5	122
	72	9·7	123 and 124
	73	9·8	125 and 126
	74	9·9	127
Unit 10	75	10·1	128
	76	10·2	129
	77	10·3	130 and 131
	78	10·4	132
	79	10·5	133 and 134
	80	10·6	135 and 136
Unit 11	81	11·1	137 and 138
	82	11·2	139
	83	11·3	140
	84	11·4	141 and 142
	85	11·5	143 and 144
	86	11·6	145 and 146
	87	11·7	147
Unit 12	88	12·1	148
	89	12·2	149 and 150
	90	12·3	151 and 152
	91	12·4	153
	92	12·5	154 and 155
	93	12·6	156

Practice Sets Answer Key

Practice Set 1

1. 15	**2.** 4	**3.** 6
4. 4	**5.** 4	**6.** 8
7. 4	**8.** 13	**9.** 8
10. 9	**11.** 12	**12.** 14
13. 13	**14.** 5	**15.** 9
16. 10	**17.** 7	**18.** 9
19. 11	**20.** 8	**21.** 4
22. 10	**23.** 4	**24.** 11
25. 10	**26.** 8	**27.** 12
28. 11	**29.** 12	**30.** 14
31. 3	**32.** 8	**33.** 9
34. 11	**35.** 7	**36.** 6
37. 2	**38.** 11	**39.** 0
40. 14	**41.** 10	**42.** 3
43. 11	**44.** 10	**45.** 5

Practice Set 2

1. D	**2.** A	**3.** B
4. C	**5.** 6,873	

6-10. Answers vary. Sample answers given.

6. $(5 * 6) + 8$; $76 \div 2$; $(50 - 20) + 8$

7. $(6 * 2) - 5$; $21 \div 3$; $(9 \div 3) + 4$

8. $(50 \div 2) + (7 * 2) + 3$; $84 \div 2$; $(100 \div 2) - 8$

9. $(10 * 10) + 11$; $(50 * 2) + (6 * 2) - 1$; $222 \div 2$

10. $(500 \div 2) - 32$; $(100 * 2) + (9 * 2)$; $300 - (41 * 2)$

11. $7 \rightarrow 21$; $11 \rightarrow 33$; $15 \rightarrow \mathbf{45}$

12. Rule: **out = in ÷ 2 or Halve; 18 → 9;** $24 \rightarrow \mathbf{12}$

13. a. 35 gal	**b.** 175 gal	**c.** 1,820 gal
14. 1	**15.** 34	**16.** 101
17. 4,561	**18.** 210	**19.** 695
20. 10,001	**21.** 43	**22.** 90
23. 121	**24.** 13	**25.** 200

Practice Set 3

1. $\angle ABC$	**2.** $\angle IHG$ or $\angle H$
3. H	**4.** $\overline{AB}$, $\overline{BC}$
5. B	**6.** $\angle CBA$ or $\angle B$

7. right angle

8. Students draw a line connecting points D and G; $DGFE$

9. $\angle ABC > \angle GFH$; Answers vary. Sample answer: The distance between points A and C is 3 units. The distance between points G and H is only two units.

10. > **11.** < **12.** < **13.** >

Practice Set 4

1. D	**2.** B	**3.** A	**4.** C

5. square; Answers vary. Sample answer: The square is also a rectangle because opposite sides are congruent and all 4 angles are congruent.

6. 8	**7.** 7	**8.** 57
9. 800	**10.** 16	**11.** 113
12. 64	**13.** 0	**14.** 280
15. 7	**16.** 450	**17.** 1,060

18. $1 \rightarrow \mathbf{5} \rightarrow 25 \rightarrow 125 \rightarrow \mathbf{625}$

19. Rule: **÷ 2 or Halve;** $128 \rightarrow \mathbf{64} \rightarrow 32 \rightarrow 16 \rightarrow \mathbf{8} \rightarrow 4$

20. $75 \rightarrow \mathbf{60} \rightarrow 45 \rightarrow \mathbf{30} \rightarrow 15 \rightarrow \mathbf{0}$

21. $3 \rightarrow \mathbf{9} \rightarrow 27 \rightarrow \mathbf{81} \rightarrow \mathbf{243} \rightarrow \mathbf{729}$

22. $60 \rightarrow \mathbf{52} \rightarrow \mathbf{44} \rightarrow \mathbf{36} \rightarrow 28 \rightarrow \mathbf{20}$

Practice Set 5

1. B, C, E, F

2. $2 + 9 = 11$; $9 + 2 = 11$; $11 - 2 = 9$; $11 - 9 = 2$

3. $8 + 9 = 17$; $9 + 8 = 17$; $17 - 8 = 9$; $17 - 9 = 8$

4. $1 + 6 = 7$; $6 + 1 = 7$; $7 - 1 = 6$; $7 - 6 = 1$

5. $3 + 4 = 7$; $4 + 3 = 7$; $7 - 3 = 4$; $7 - 4 = 3$

6. $4 + 6 = 10$; $6 + 4 = 10$; $10 - 4 = 6$; $10 - 6 = 4$

7. $6 + 7 = 13$; $7 + 6 = 13$; $13 - 7 = 6$; $13 - 6 = 7$

8. $(105 - 70) + 15 = 50$

9. $18 - (8 + 3) = 7$

10. $(50 - 16) + 9 = 43$

11. $338 - (81 + 42) = 215$

12. 3	**13.** 49	**14.** 20
15. 6	**16.** 12	**17.** 8
18. 48	**19.** 36	**20.** 81
21. 7	**22.** 36	**23.** 63
24. 12	**25.** 8	**26.** 42
27. 32	**28.** 6	**29.** 45
30. 32	**31.** 24	**32.** 8
33. 28	**34.** 4	**35.** 10
36. 18	**37.** 8	**38.** 42
39. 28	**40.** 4	**41.** 72
42. 54	**43.** 6	**44.** 14
45. 56	**46.** 21	**47.** 9
48. 35	**49.** 18	**50.** 2

Practice Sets Answer Key *continued*

51. 12   **52.** 72   **53.** 7
54. 45   **55.** 5   **56.** 16

Practice Set 6

1. A, C, E
2. Answers vary. Sample answer: Figures A, C, and E each have sides that are all congruent and angles that are all congruent.

3. 90   **4.** 99   **5.** 96
6. 23   **7.** 8   **8.** 81
9. 51   **10.** 19   **11.** 296
12. 45   **13.** 6,000   **14.** 652
15. 49   **16.** 105

Practice Set 7

1. B   **2.** C   **3.** A   **4.** D
5. 4   **6.** 4   **7.** 2
8. 3 → 6 → 18 → **36** → 108 → **216** → **648** → **1,296** → **3,888**

Practice Set 8

1. 4 * 4 = 16 square units
2. 3 * 8 = 24 square units
3. 2   **4.** 4   **5.** 0
6. 8   **7.** 1
8. 6 * 7 = 42; 7 * 6 = 42; 42 ÷ 6 = 7; 42 ÷ 7 = 6
9. 3 * 9 = 27; 9 * 3 = 27; 27 ÷ 3 = 9; 27 ÷ 9 = 3
10. 4 * 8 = 32; 8 * 4 = 32; 32 ÷ 4 = 8; 32 ÷ 8 = 4
11. 5 * 9 = 45; 9 * 5 = 45; 45 ÷ 9 = 5; 45 ÷ 5 = 9
12. 2 * 8 = 16; 8 * 2 = 16; 16 ÷ 8 = 2; 16 ÷ 2 = 8
13. 4 * 7 = 28; 7 * 4 = 28; 28 ÷ 4 = 7; 28 ÷ 7 = 4
14. 3 * 25 = 75

Practice Set 9

1. B-2   **2.** D-4
3. Check students' drawings.
4. Answers vary. Sample answer: Amy lives closer to the library. It is 3 blocks away. The school is 7 blocks away.
5. Answers vary. Check students' drawings.
6. D   **7.** C

8. Answers vary. Sample answer: Even though new items are added to the museum, an estimate will still be correct.
9. square   **10.** rectangle
11. trapezoid
12. 950; 951; **952; 953;** 954; **955; 956; 957;** 958
13. **5,020;** 5,060; **5,100; 5,140;** 5,180; 5,220; **5,260; 5,300**
14. 10,400; **10,375; 10,350;** 10,325; **10,300; 10,275;** 10,250
15. 2,335; **2,435;** 2,535; 2,635; **2,735; 2,835;** 2,935

Practice Set 10

1. Answers vary. Sample answer: $3 * 3 * 3$; $(50 ÷ 2) + 2$; $(7 * 3) + (6 * 1)$; $\frac{54}{2}$; $(5 * 4) + 7$; 3^3
2. Answers vary. Sample answer: $25 * 5$; $5 * 5 * 5$; $\frac{250}{2}$; $(10 * 10) + (5 * 5)$; $(60 * 2) + 5$; 5^3

3. 36   **4.** 72   **5.** 35
6. 70   **7.** 44   **8.** 81
9. 48   **10.** 35   **11.** 99
12. 24   **13.** 88   **14.** 96
15. 110   **16.** 32   **17.** 6
18. 45   **19.** 77   **20.** 84
21. 2   **22.** 5   **23.** 5
24. 4   **25.** 5   **26.** 5

Practice Set 11

1. 742   **2.** 8,231   **3.** 60,573
4. 96,814   **5.** 803,301   **6.** 4,930,490
7. 93,728   **8.** 60   **9.** 77
10. 12   **11.** 18   **12.** 40
13. 10   **14.** 55   **15.** 120
16. 7   **17.** 48   **18.** 56
19. 7   **20.** 9   **21.** 42
22. 9   **23.** 10   **24.** 99
25. 11   **26.** 32   **27.** 110
28. 72   **29.** 121   **30.** 132
31. 28   **32.** 192   **33.** 9
34. 48   **35.** 9   **36.** 5
37. 4   **38.** 6   **39.** 24
40. 60   **41.** 36   **42.** 11
43. 300   **44.** 56   **45.** 12
46. 2   **47.** 11   **48.** 6
49. 9   **50.** 4   **51.** 2
52. 21

Practice Set 12

1. 24,968   2. 76,614   3. 6,902
4. twelve thousand, seven hundred forty-three
5. eight thousand, fifty-four
6. sixty-nine thousand, two hundred thirty-one
7. four thousand, seven hundred eighty-two

8. 73	9. 81	10. 64
11. 1,260	12. 0	13. 50.8
14. 7.68	15. 3.39	16. 99
17. 47	18. 120	19. 42

Practice Set 13

1. 24	2. 7	3. 0
4. 7	5. 0	6. 16,547
7. 8.2	8. 7.9	

9. twenty-one thousand, eight hundred ninety-four
10. fourteen and one tenth
11. forty-eight thousand, five hundred sixty-three
12. nine hundred three
13. $15 \rightarrow \textbf{300}$; $25 \rightarrow \textbf{500}$; $100 \rightarrow \textbf{2,000}$
14. Rule: **out = in − 3.5**; $14 \rightarrow \textbf{10.5}$; $16.5 \rightarrow \textbf{13}$
15. Rule: **out = in ÷ 4**; $160 \rightarrow \textbf{40}$; $360 \rightarrow 90$; $2,400 \rightarrow \textbf{600}$
16. $3 \rightarrow \textbf{30}$; $6 \rightarrow \textbf{60}$; $9 \rightarrow 90$; $12 \rightarrow 120$; $15 \rightarrow \textbf{150}$
17. $(6 * 11) − 7 = 59$
18. $2.2 = 8 − (3 + 2.8)$
19. $330 − (150 − 60) = 240$
20. $18 = 2 * (5.4 + 3.6)$
21. $(7 * 2.1) + (5 * 12) = 74.7$
22. $230 = (4 * 60) − 10$
23. $3 * (9 + 3) − 4 = 32$
24. $584 = (11 * 50) + 34$
25. $12 ÷ (4 + 2) * 3 = 6$
26. $(6 + 3) * 2 − 4 = 14$

Practice Set 14

1.

No. of Students

Number of Hours of Practice Each Week

2. 8   3. 2   4. 6   5. 5
6. 4.15 hours; Answers vary. Sample answer: I multiplied the number of students by the number of hours for each row. Then I added all the products together and divided by the total number of students.
7. $\textbf{100} \rightarrow \textbf{200} \rightarrow \textbf{300} \rightarrow \textbf{400} \rightarrow 500$
8. Rule: **÷ 4**; $512 \rightarrow 128 \rightarrow 32 \rightarrow \textbf{8} \rightarrow 2$
9. 49,667
10. $387 ÷ 10$; $(4 * 9) + (9 * 0.3)$; $40 − 1.3$; $(80 ÷ 4) + 18.7$; $(15 * 2) + (17.4 ÷ 2)$; $77.4 ÷ 2$; $9 * 4.3$
11. $10,000 − 2,951$; $(1,000 * 7) + (7 * 7)$; $(400 * 20) − 951$; $1,007 * 7$; $21,147 ÷ 3$; $(7 * 1,000) + (4 * 10) + 9$; $7,050 − 1$
12. $16.24 ÷ 2$; $(5 * 2) − (0.94 * 2)$; $2.03 * 4$; $(4 * 2) + (0.4 * 0.3)$; $4.06 * 2$; $(3 * 3) − 0.88$; $4.06 ÷ 0.5$
13. $2 * 3 = 6$ 14. $5 * 8 = 40$
15. $2 * 10 = 20$ 16. $7 * 9 = 63$

Practice Set 15

1. 353	2. 818	3. 2,455
4. 1,212	5. 1,471	6. 4,040
7. 1,411	8. 13,702	9. 14,794
10. 90,212	11. 3	12. 9
13. 8	14. 8	15. 9
16. 70	17. $12.00	18. $2.80
19. $24.50		

Practice Set 16

1. 5	2. 1	3. 4
4. 3	5. 8 cm	6. 6 cm
7. 7 cm	8. 3 cm	

9. $\textbf{2:05} \rightarrow \textbf{3:00} \rightarrow 3:55 \rightarrow 4:50 \rightarrow 5:45$
10. $\$2.20 \rightarrow \textbf{\$2.70} \rightarrow \textbf{\$1.95} \rightarrow \textbf{\$1.20} \rightarrow \textbf{\$1.70} \rightarrow \textbf{\$0.95} \rightarrow \textbf{\$1.45}$
11. $50 \rightarrow \textbf{5,000} \rightarrow 250 \rightarrow \textbf{25,000} \rightarrow 1,250 \rightarrow \textbf{125,000} \rightarrow \textbf{6,250}$
12. $8 \rightarrow 40 \rightarrow 4 \rightarrow 20 \rightarrow 2 \rightarrow 10 \rightarrow 1 \rightarrow 5 \rightarrow 0.5$

Practice Set 17

1. 55	2. 338	3. 189	4. 21
5. 388	6. 348	7. 58	8. 16
9. 138	10. 776	11. 19	12. 33

13. 9, 17, **25, 33, 41, 49, 57,** 65
14. 0.2, **0.4, 0.6,** 0.8, **1.0 or 1,** 1.2, 1.4, 1.6
15. $\frac{1}{7}, \frac{2}{7}, \frac{3}{7}, \frac{4}{7}, \frac{5}{7}, \frac{6}{7}, 1, 1\frac{1}{7}, 1\frac{2}{7}$

Practice Sets Answer Key *continued*

16. 15

17. $\frac{6}{15}$ or $\frac{2}{5}$

18. $\frac{4}{15}$

19. $\frac{5}{15}$ or $\frac{1}{3}$

20. Answers vary. Sample answer: I counted all the bananas to find the numerator. I counted all the fruit to find the denominator. Then I reduced the fraction by dividing both the numerator and the denominator by 5.

21. 268   **22.** 424   **23.** 28

24. 4,050   **25.** 11,389   **26.** 2,151

27. 0   **28.** 609   **29.** 652

30. 2,560   **31.** 70   **32.** 6,528

Practice Set 18

1. Rule: ÷ 3; **27 → 9; 36 → 12**

2. 8 → **40**; 10 → **50**; 12 → **60**; 14 → **70**

3. Rule: × 4; 30 → **120**; 40 → 160

4. 4 → 32; **6** → **48**; **8** → **64**; **10** → 80

5. 4 blue cubes; 4 red cubes; 4 green cubes

6. 5 blue cubes; 5 red cubes; 2 green cubes

7. Answers vary. Sample answer: I divided the 12 cubes into 2 groups of 6. I took 1 cube from each group because 1 out of every 6 cubes is green. That left 2 equal groups of 5. One group is red, and the other group is blue.

Practice Set 19

1. 54   **2.** 49   **3.** 3

4. 96   **5.** 11   **6.** 20

7. 44   **8.** 8   **9.** 60

10. 110   **11.** 9   **12.** 9

13. 63   **14.** 6   **15.** 27

16. 84   **17.** 18   **18.** 36

19. 81   **20.** 11   **21.** 42

22. 48   **23.** 7   **24.** 12

25. 32   **26.** 7   **27.** 12

28. 40   **29.** 121   **30.** 24

31. 132   **32.** 6   **33.** 6

34. 21   **35.** 48   **36.** 11

37. 48   **38.** 33   **39.** 10

40. 8   **41.** 108   **42.** 28

43. 24   **44.** 11   **45.** 7

46. $11.14   **47.** 16

48. Yes. They have $0.44 left over.

49. about $0.25   **50.** about $0.50

Practice Set 20

1. 5   **2.** 6   **3.** 42

4. 10   **5.** 2   **6.** 9

7. 8   **8.** 14   **9.** 4

10. 5   **11.** 28   **12.** 9

13. 9   **14.** 44   **15.** 131

16. Answers vary. Check students' riddles.

Practice Set 21

1. 9; 9 * 7 = 63; 7 * 9 = 63; $\frac{63}{9}$ = 7; $\frac{63}{7}$ = 9

2. 48; 8 * 6 = 48; 6 * 8 = 48; $\frac{48}{6}$ = 8; $\frac{48}{8}$ = 6

3. 9; 6 * 9 = 54; 9 * 6 = 54; $\frac{54}{9}$ = 6; $\frac{54}{6}$ = 9

4.

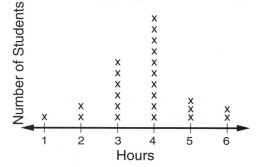

Student Data on Homework Time

5. Answers vary. Sample answer: 4 hours

6. 10   **7.** 2,400   **8.** 100

9. 1,600   **10.** 50   **11.** 8,000

12. 2   **13.** 20   **14.** 4,900

15. 180   **16.** 900   **17.** 810

18. $4.77   **19.** $90   **20.** 1,400 m

21. $\frac{3}{12}$ or $\frac{1}{4}$ **22.** $\frac{12}{12}$ or 1

23. $\frac{8}{12}$ or $\frac{2}{3}$ **24.** $\frac{9}{12}$ or $\frac{3}{4}$

Practice Set 22

1. 9; 5 * 9 = 45; 9 * 5 = 45; 45 ÷ 9 = 5; 45 ÷ 5 = 9

2. 3; 3 * 12 = 36; 12 * 3 = 36; 36 ÷ 12 = 3; 36 ÷ 3 = 12

3. 42; 7 * 6 = 42; 6 * 7 = 42; 42 ÷ 6 = 7; 42 ÷ 7 = 6

4. 60; 4 * 15 = 60; 15 * 4 = 60; 60 ÷ 15 = 4; 60 ÷ 4 = 15

5. $\frac{3}{8}$ **6.** $\frac{3}{6}$ or $\frac{1}{2}$ **7.** $\frac{2}{6}$ or $\frac{1}{3}$

8. $\frac{1}{4}$ **9.** $\frac{40}{100}$ or $\frac{4}{10}$ or $\frac{2}{5}$

10. $\frac{90}{100}$ or $\frac{9}{10}$

Practice Set 23

1. $174,000 - 22,300$; about 151,700 square miles
2. $8,200 - 923$; about 7,277 feet
3. about 9 times
4. $1,100 - 100$; about 1,000 types
5. No; Answers vary. Sample answer: The data show that there are more types of fish in the Red Sea. It does not tell whether or not there are more actual fish.
6. 3 pints   7. $2\frac{1}{2}$ gallons   8. 12 yards
9. 10 feet, 8 inches or $10\frac{2}{3}$ feet
10. 6,240   11. 4,173
12. 11,510   13. 2,597

Practice Set 24

1. 2,660 miles; $1,714 + 946 = 2,660$
2. 341 T-shirts; $683 - 342 = 341$
3. 114 cm; $257 - 143 = 114$
4. Answers vary. Sample answer: "How many more" means subtract to find the difference.
5. 1,266   6. 107   7. 358
8. 1,840   9. 1,008   10. 818
11. 4,237   12. 288   13. $1.63
14. $3.22   15. $16.40   16. $148.25
17. a. 2   b. 4
   c. Answers vary. Sample answer: The total would probably be 20, since the class read an average of 4 hours per day.

Practice Set 25

1. F   2. T   3. F   4. F
5. ?   6. T   7. T   8. F
9. $\frac{1}{4}$ 10. $\frac{3}{4}$ 11. 0 or $\frac{0}{4}$ 12. 282
13. 189   14. 1,070   15. 4,921
16. 920   17. 392   18. 670
19. 4,500   20. 7, 14, 21, 28, 35
21. 3, 6, 9, 12, 15   22. 4, 8, 12, 16, 20
23. 9, 18, 27, 36, 45

Practice Set 26

1. $(6 * 8) - 3 = 45$ 2. $22 = (8 + 3) * 2$
3. $33 - (15 - 6) = 24$ 4. $(54 - 10) + 8 = 52$
5. $(3 * 8) + (2 * 11) = 46$
6. $30 = (4 * 6) + 6$
7. $(2 * 2) + (7 * 8) = 60$
8. $489 = 5 * (25 + 75) - 11$
9. a. 360 ft   b. 720 ft

10. 8,421
11. one thousand, six hundred three

Practice Set 27

1. 27; $27 + 8 = 35$
2. 6; $4 * 6 = 24$
3. 143; $140 + 3 = 143$
4. 49; $49 / 7 = 7$
5. 260; $260 - 60 = 200$
6. 12; $68 + 12 = 80$
7. 7; $6 * 7 = 42$
8. 7; $70 / 7 = 10$
9. $204 = (7 * 20) + (75 - 11)$
10. $7 * (9 - 4) = 35$
11. $42 = (3 + 3) * 7$
12. $(31 - 15) - 6 = 10$
13. $(54 - 10) + 8 = 52$
14. $(7 * 8) + (3 * 11) = 89$
15. 4,240   16. 709   17. 793
18. 0   19. 16,398   20. 1
21. 560   22. 27   23. 990
24. 150   25. a. $\frac{3}{4}$ b. $\frac{1}{4}$ c. 1
26. 26   27. 26   28. 5
29. 4   30. $\frac{4}{6}$ or $\frac{2}{3}$ 31. 52
32. 9   33. $\frac{2}{6}$ or $\frac{1}{3}$ 34. $\frac{3}{5}$

Practice Sets Answer Key *continued*

Practice Set 28

1. **−16, −8**, 0, 8, **16**, 24, **32**
2. 2, 24, **46, 68**, 90, **112, 134**
3. **0**, 11, **22**, 33, **44, 55**, 66
4. 0.2, 1.2, 2.10, 2.2
5. 0.04, 0.23, 1.2, 5.1
6. 1.4, 1.41, 2.14, 4.01
7. 0.59, 1.95, 9.5, 19.5
8. 0.03, 0.3, 3.03, 3.3
9. 5.02, 5.12, 5.20, 5.21
10. 339
11. 1,229
12. 508
13. 320
14. 412
15. 90
16. 351
17. 58
18. 399
19. 10,869
20. 49,000
21. 1,699
22. 28
23. 16 → **56** → **96** → **136** → **101** → **141** → **106** → **146** → **186**
24. 5 → **10** → **20** → **40** → 8 → **16** → **32** → **64** → **128**
25. 0, **0.001, 0.002, 0.003, 0.004**, 0.005, **0.006, 0.007, 0.008, 0.009**, 0.01 or 0.010
26. 0.005
27. three hundredths
28. seventy-six hundredths

Practice Set 29

1. potatoes
2. tomatoes
3. about 5 kg
4.

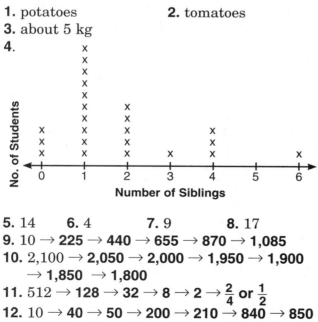

5. 14
6. 4
7. 9
8. 17
9. 10 → **225** → **440** → **655** → **870** → **1,085**
10. 2,100 → **2,050** → **2,000** → **1,950** → **1,900** → **1,850** → **1,800**
11. 512 → **128** → **32** → **8** → **2** → $\frac{2}{4}$ **or** $\frac{1}{2}$
12. 10 → **40** → **50** → **200** → **210** → **840** → **850** → **860** → **3,440**
13. 729 → **243** → **81** → **27** → **9** → **3**

Practice Set 30

1. 28.2
2. 3.4
3. 5.3
4. 12.14
5. 4.29
6. 1.49
7. 1.48
8. 1.44
9. 22.4
10. 0.36
11. 4 inches, 11 centimeters
12. 3 inches, 8 centimeters
13. 6 inches, 17 centimeters
14. 9 → **1,800**; 12 → **2,400**; 14 → **2,800**; 35 → **7,000**
15. Rule: **out = in** + **7**$\frac{1}{2}$ **or in = out** − **7**$\frac{1}{2}$; **12**$\frac{1}{2}$ → **20**; **13**$\frac{1}{2}$ → **21**
16. **a.** 1   **b.** $28   **c.** 7   **d.** $17   **e.** 68
17. **a.** 0   **b.** 1   **c.** $42   **d.** 6   **e.** $16   **f.** 7 * 16 = 112
18. **a.** 1   **b.** $81   **c.** 1   **d.** $21   **e.** 3   **f.** $3

Practice Set 31

1. $13.18
2. $38.22
3. $8.85
4. $6.57
5. $2.25
6. $8.48
7. $36.56
8. $9.71
9. $29.18
10. $30.21
11. Rule: *** 12**; 5 → **60**, 11 → **132**, 15 → **180**
12. Rule: **+ 16; 28** → 44, 35 → **51**
13. Answers vary. Sample answer: (5 * 2) * (19 * 2); 95 * 4; (250 * 2) − (60 * 2); (15 * 20) + (4 * 20)
14. Answers vary. Sample answer: (10 * 10) + (25 * 3) + 1; 200 − 24; (5 * 30) + (5 * 6) − (2 * 2); 1,000 − 824
15. Answers vary. Sample answer: (4 * 1,000) + (2 * 100) + (1 * 10) + (8 * 1); 2 * 2,109; 5,000 − 782; (70 * 60) + (9 * 2)

Practice Sets Answer Key *continued*

Practice Set 32

Base-10 Blocks	Fraction Notation	Decimal Notation
1. $\Box\Box$ |||||	$\frac{258}{1000}$	**0.258**
2. $\Box\Box\Box$	$\frac{3}{10}$	**0.3**
3. $\Box\Box\Box$ ||||| ||||	$\frac{39}{100}$	0.39
4. $\Box\Box$	$1\frac{10}{100}$	1.10
5. |||||||||	$\frac{90}{1,000}$	0.090
6.	$\frac{8}{1000}$	0.008
7. $\Box\Box\Box\Box\Box$ ||||.	$\frac{541}{1,000}$	**0.541**

Practice Set 33

1. 3 cm; 0.03m **2.** 1 cm; 0.01m
3. 5 cm; 0.05m **4.** 8 cm; 0.08m
5. 6 cm; 0.06m
6. F **7.** T **8.** F **9.** F **10.** F **11.** T
12. 260,453 **13.** 286.38 **14.** 314,691
15. 1,074,968 **16.** 6,709,845 **17.** 186
18. 144 **19.** 9 **20.** 2,800
21. 40 **22.** 600 **23.** 12
24. 2 **25.** 350 **26.** 1,800
27. 600 **28.** 1,440 **29.** $13.00
30. Answers vary. Sample answer:
I multiplied the number of greeting cards by the price of one card. Then I placed the decimal and dollar sign in the product.
31. 110 dollars **32.** 4,600 meters
33. 40 blocks **34.** 1,760 yards

Practice Set 34

1. 5 m **2.** 810 cm **3.** 720 mm **4.** 1.5 m
5. 35 m **6.** 0.63 m **7.** 98 mm **8.** 3.75 m
9. Answers vary. Sample answer: There are 100 centimeters in one meter, so I divided 375 by 100.
10. 873 **11.** 3,199 **12.** 8,955 **13.** 4,721
14. 569 **15.** 725 **16.** 10,199 **17.** 399
18. 1,170 **19.** 2,062 **20.** 1,411 **21.** 184
22. 3,087 **23.** 458 **24.** 815

Practice Set 35

1. 894.096 **2.** 41 mm
3. Answers vary. Sample answer: Because the picture is 2 times bigger than the actual size, I divided 4 by 2 to find the actual size.
4. 43 mm **5.** 3 cm **6.** 0.6 cm **7.** 43 mm
8. Rule: **out = in + 8.25 or in = out − 8.25**;
12.5 → **20.75**; 14.5 → **22.75**; 54.10 → **62.35**
9. 900 → **300**; 1,200 → **400**; 1,500 → **500**;
1,800 → **600**
10. $(26 \div 2) - 7 = 6$ **11.** $41.2 = (7 * 6) - 0.8$
12. $(130 - 15) - 60 = 55$
13. $118 = 2 * (55.7 + 3.3)$
14. $(10 * 2.1) + (5 * 12.2) = 82$
15. $30 = (6 * 20) - 90$
16. $11 * (12 + 7 - 4) = 165$
17. $99 = 11 * (50 - 41)$
18. $(50 + 300) \div 5 = 70$
19. $200 * (2.6 - 1.1) + 5 = 305$

Practice Sets Answer Key *continued*

Practice Set 36

1. 320   2. 3,000   3. 140
4. 200   5. 4,200   6. 270
7. 1,600   8. 3,200   9. 36,000
10. 6 out of 21   11. 3 out of 21 or 1 out of 7
12. 12 out of 21 or 4 out of 7
13. 0 out of 21
14. 49   15. 48
16. 45   17. 45   18. 0.45
19. 0.53   20. 0.41   21. 0.8 or 0.80
22.

Birthday Months

Bar graph — x-axis: Months (Jan., Feb., March, April, May, June, July, Aug., Sept., Oct., Nov., Dec.); y-axis: Number of Birthdays (0–10).

23. March   24. January and November
25. 2.92   26. 2.5
27. 2   28. 5

Practice Set 37

1. 13,200   2. 9,100   3. 8,900
4. 19,500   5. 19,700   6. 20,800
7. 14,700   8. 18,200   9. $2.64
10. 5   11. 4   12. 49
13. 36   14. 720   15. 25
16. 16   17. 56   18. 30
19. 1   20. 4   21. 8
22. 45,392   23. 459,703   24. 6,004,602

Practice Set 38

1. 400 cans; 10 * 40 = 400
2. 600 ounces; 100 * 6 = 600
3. 1,000 people; 20 * 50 = 1,000
4. about 35 pounds
5. about 1,820 pounds
6. about 1 ton   7. About 4 tons
8. more
9. about 300 million tons

10. Answers vary. Sample answer: I multiplied the number of people in the United States by the number of pounds of trash per person each day.

11. Answers vary. Sample answer: XV; 5 * 3; 45 ÷ 3; 30 − 15
12. Answers vary. Sample answer: C; 10 * 10; 1,000 ÷ 10; 200 − 100
13. Answers vary. Sample answer: LIV; 9 * 6; 60 − 6; 108 ÷ 2
14. Answers vary. Sample answer: LXXIII; $(25 * 3) - 2$; $(8 * 9) + 1$; $\frac{146}{2}$
15. False   16. True   17. False
18. False   19. 4,723

Practice Set 39

1.
100s	10s	1s
	8	2
*		9
7	2	0
+ 1	1	8
7	3	8

2.
100s	10s	1s
1	3	5
*		6
6	0	0
1	8	0
+	3	0
8	1	0

3.
1000s	100s	10s	1s
		5	4	5
*			3
1	5	0	0
	1	2	0
+		1	5
1,	6	3	5

4. 200 * 6 = 1200; (1000s); 214 * 6 = 1,284 pennies
5. 100 * 4 = 400; (100s); 130 * 4 = 520 minutes
6. 175,342   7. 27.8
8. 3,082,602

Practice Sets Answer Key *continued*

Practice Set 40

1. 282	**2.** 445	**3.** 351
4. 1,656	**5.** 1,710	**6.** 1,426
7. 6,519	**8.** 11,034	**9.** 92
10. 18	**11.** 90	**12.** 315
13. 18	**14.** 55	**15.** 3,000
16. 27	**17.** 36	**18.** 8
19. 11	**20.** 3	**21.** 15
22. 4	**23.** 98	**24.** 102

25. a. $\frac{1}{4}$ **b.** $\frac{4}{4}$ or 1   **c.** $\frac{2}{4}$ or $\frac{1}{2}$

26. a. $\frac{3}{4}$ **b.** $\frac{1}{4}$ **c.** 0 or $\frac{0}{4}$

   d. $\frac{4}{4}$ or 1   **e.** $\frac{1}{2}$

Practice Set 41

1. 928

2. 6,527

3.

Favorite Sports

4. 9,780	**5.** 879	**6.** 533
7. 1,560	**8.** 6,293	**9.** 3,663
10. 198	**11.** 12,519	**12.** 875
13. 340	**14.** 35	**15.** 645

16. 27

17. No; Answers vary. Sample answer: I need to know what the starting temperature was.

18. $412 = 70 * (5 + 1) - 8$

19. $(6 * 10) - 5 = 55$

20. $81 = (7 + 2) * 9$

21. $(39 - 16) - 4 = 19$

22. $44 - (13 + 23) = 8$

23. $(8 * 5) + (2 * 18) = 76$

24. $135 = 9 * (9 + 6)$

25. $4 * (3 + 7) * 6 = 240$

Practice Set 42

1. 2,718,920   **2.** 769,231   **3.** 18.978

4. eighteen million, five hundred sixty-four thousand, two hundred ninety

5. forty-eight and one hundred twenty-eight thousandths

6. five million, seven hundred seventy-three thousand, nine hundred sixty-three

7. one hundred two thousand, seven hundred fifty-six

8. $2.89   **9.** $7.95   **10.** $137

11. $1.77   **12.** $12.42   **13.** $56.15

Practice Set 43

1. $10 * 10$; 1 thousand; 10,000; 10^5

2. 10[hundreds]; 10^4; $10 * 10 * 10 * 10 * 10$; 1 million

3. 10^2; $10 * 10 * 10$; 10 [thousands]; 100,000

4. 10[tenths]; $10 * 10$; 1 thousand; 10^5

5. 10^3	**6.** 10^5	**7.** 10^6
8. 10^0	**9.** 5	**10.** 4
11. 1	**12.** 4	**13.** 8
14. 2	**15.** 0	**16.** 18
17. 3	**18.** 3	**19.** $\frac{1}{2}$
20. 12	**21.** 140	**22.** 186
23. 1,060	**24.** 61	**25.** 846
26. 5,000	**27.** 1,316	**28.** 1,191

29. about $6; Answers vary. Sample answer: $(2 * 1) + (2 * 1) + (2 * 1) = 6$

30. $3.34   **31.** 35¢ per card

32. Yes; Answers vary. Sample answer: Each roll is less than $2. $2 + $2 + $2 = $6.

Practice Set 44

1. 8,133 ft

2. Japan

3. a. Japan   **b.** England

4. $8,133 - 5,600$; 2,533 ft

5. Steel Force and Mamba

Practice Sets Answer Key *continued*

Practice Set 45

1.

gifts	inches of ribbon per gift	inches of ribbon in all
6	12	72

$72 \div 6 = 12$; 12 inches

2.

days	miles per day	miles in all
4	300	1,200

$1200 \div 300 = 4$; 4 days

3.

trays	CDs per tray	CDs in all
9	30	270

$270 \div 30 = 9$; 9 trays

4.

people	balloons per person	balloons in all
3	28	84

$84 \div 3 = 28$; 28 balloons

5. 16   **6.** 36   **7.** 7
8. 54   **9.** 35   **10.** 18
11. 54   **12.** 3   **13.** 49
14. 15   **15.** 56   **16.** 25
17. 9   **18.** 2   **19.** 18
20. 48   **21.** 21   **22.** 6
23. 54   **24.** 40   **25.** 63
26. 24   **27.** 6   **28.** 16
29. 45   **30.** 28   **31.** 20
32. 3   **33.** 4   **34.** 81
35. equilateral
36. the three angles
37. 27 cm

Practice Set 46

1. 80; $80 * 9 = 720$; $9 * 80 = 720$;
$\frac{720}{80} = 9$; $\frac{720}{9} = 80$

2. 8; $50 * 8 = 400$; $8 * 50 = 400$;
$\frac{400}{50} = 8$; $\frac{400}{8} = 50$

3. 500; $5 * 500 = 2,500$; $500 * 5 = 2,500$;
$\frac{2,500}{500} = 5$; $\frac{2,500}{5} = 500$

4. 60; $60 * 80 = 4,800$; $80 * 60 = 4,800$;
$\frac{4,800}{80} = 60$; $\frac{4,800}{60} = 80$

5. 900; $900 * 30 = 27,000$;
$30 * 900 = 27,000$; $\frac{27,000}{900} = 30$;
$\frac{27,000}{30} = 900$

6. 600; $60 * 600 = 36,000$;
$600 * 60 = 36,000$; $\frac{36,000}{600} = 60$;
$\frac{36,000}{60} = 600$

7. 1,601   **8.** 189   **9.** 1,302   **10.** 890
11. 1,206   **12.** 722   **13.** 1,047   **14.** 1,141
15. $1.58   **16.** $3.67   **17.** $26.35   **18.** $247
19. $\frac{1}{3}, \frac{2}{3}, \frac{3}{3}$ or 1, $\frac{4}{3}$ or $1\frac{1}{3}$, $\frac{5}{3}$ or $1\frac{2}{3}$, $\frac{6}{3}$ or 2,
$\frac{7}{3}$ or $2\frac{1}{3}$, $\frac{8}{3}$ or $2\frac{2}{3}$
20. 0.5, 0.8, 1.1, **1.4, 1.7, 2.0,** 2.3, **2.6**
21. 2, **4,** 6, 8, **10, 12, 14, 16**

Practice Set 47

1. 31   **2.** 25 R4   **3.** 39 R4
4. 22 R5   **5.** 65   **6.** 51 R1
7. 9 R3   **8.** 24 R5   **9.** 19 R4
10. 31 R3   **11.** 23 R3   **12.** 14 R11
13. a. 2   **b.** $8   **c.** 1
   d. $21   **e.** $168 \div 8 = 21
14. 105   **15.** 826   **16.** 4,674
17. 679   **18.** 6   **19.** 4
20. 5   **21.** 6   **22.** 8
23. 3   **24.** 4   **25.** 10
26. 108   **27.** 9   **28.** 11
29. 4   **30.** 7   **31.** 15
32. 6   **33.** 11   **34.** 4
35. 5   **36.** 6   **37.** 8
38. 3   **39.** 8   **40.** 8
41. 24   **42.** 12   **43.** 9
44. 9   **45.** 4   **46.** 6
47. 13

Practice Set 48

1. hundreds   **2.** tens   **3.** thousands
4. tens   **5.** hundreds   **6.** tens
7. hundreds   **8.** tens   **9.** tens
10. hundreds
11. $516 \div 4 = 129$; 129 cards
12. $354 \div 6 = 59$; $59
13. $3 * 24 = 72$; 72
14. $92 * 6 = 552$; $552
15. 15   **16.** $\frac{5}{15}$ or $\frac{1}{3}$ **17.** $\frac{10}{15}$ or $\frac{2}{3}$
18. $\frac{9}{15}$ or $\frac{3}{5}$ **19.** $\frac{0}{15}$ or 0   **20.** 3
21. 4   **22.** 7   **23.** 480
24. 60   **25.** 50   **26.** 80
27. 20   **28.** $15\frac{1}{2}$ **29.** $65\frac{3}{10}$
30. $30\frac{5}{15}$ or $30\frac{1}{3}$
31. 18.5   **32.** 15.25   **33.** 500.25

Practice Set 49

1. <; 70°   **2.** >; 130°   **3.** <; 85°   **4.** <; 45°
5. false   **6.** true   **7.** false   **8.** true
9. 360°; Answers vary. Sample answer: No matter how large or small the circle is, $\frac{1}{4}$ of the circle will always be 90°, $\frac{1}{2}$ of the circle will always be 180°, and so on.

Practice Set 50

1. 90°   **2.** 180°   **3.** 18°
4. 150°   **5.** 150°   **6.** 360°
7. $50 \rightarrow 500 \rightarrow \mathbf{5{,}000} \rightarrow 50{,}000 \rightarrow \mathbf{500{,}000}$
8. $1{:}45 \rightarrow \mathbf{2{:}30} \rightarrow 3{:}15 \rightarrow \mathbf{4{:}00} \rightarrow \mathbf{4{:}45} \rightarrow \mathbf{5{:}30}$
9. $\$3.50 \rightarrow \mathbf{\$3.60} \rightarrow \mathbf{\$3.70} \rightarrow \mathbf{\$1.90} \rightarrow 10¢ \rightarrow$ **20¢** $\rightarrow$ **30¢**
10. a. She can buy 2 boxes of 16 crayons each.
   b. 3 crayons
11. 4 boxes   **12.** $6.36
13. No; Answers vary. Sample answer: The crayons cost almost $4 each. It would cost almost $20 to buy 5 boxes.
14. 87   **15.** 456   **16.** 2,970
17. 1,228   **18.** 6,020   **19.** 3,674
20.
```
· · · · · · · ·
 · · · · · · · ·
 · · · · · · · ·
 · · · · · · · ·
```

Practice Set 51

1. $1.00   **2.** $1.50   **3.** $0.50   **4.** $\frac{1}{6}$
5. 15   **6.** 56   **7.** 998
8. $3 \rightarrow \mathbf{75}$; $4 \rightarrow \mathbf{100}$; $8 \rightarrow \mathbf{200}$; $14 \rightarrow 350$; $16 \rightarrow \mathbf{400}$
9. $81 \rightarrow \mathbf{9}$; $54 \rightarrow \mathbf{6}$; $108 \rightarrow 12$; $117 \rightarrow \mathbf{13}$; $63 \rightarrow 7$
10. 142   **11.** 748   **12.** 638
13. 453   **14.** 468   **15.** 90
16. 12,870   **17.** 4,200   **18.** 4,467
19. Sample drawing:

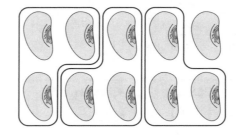

$10 \div 3$; 3 R 1

20. Sample drawing:

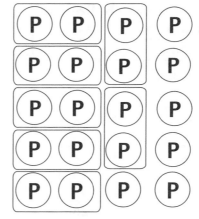

$20 \div 7$; 2 R 6

Practice Sets Answer Key *continued*

Practice Set 52

1. 500 possible outcomes   2. yes
3.

Event	Favorable Outcomes	Possible Outcomes	Probability
Picking Katie's ticket	1	500	$\frac{1}{500}$
Picking the ticket of one of the three girls	3	500	$\frac{3}{500}$
Picking the ticket of a person in their town	400	500	$\frac{400}{500}$
Picking a ticket	500	500	$\frac{500}{500}$

4. very unlikely; Answers vary. Sample answer: The number of favorable outcomes is extremely low as compared to the number of possible outcomes.
5. $700 + 200 = 900$
6. $300 + 900 = 1,200$
7. $600 + 100 = 700$
8. $400 + 1,900 = 2,300$

Practice Set 53

1. $\frac{1}{3}$ 2. $\frac{5}{6}$ 3. $\frac{3}{4}$ 4. $\frac{3}{8}$
5. $\frac{2}{5}$ 6. $\frac{1}{4}$ 7. $<$ 8. $>$
9. $<$ 10. $>$ 11. $>$ 12. $>$
13. $6\frac{5}{6}$ 14. $20\frac{1}{3}$ 15. $21\frac{3}{4}$ 16. $74\frac{1}{2}$
17. $53\frac{3}{5}$ 18. $91\frac{3}{8}$ 19. $75\frac{5}{9}$ 20. $60\frac{5}{7}$
21. 25   22. 80   23. 10
24. 3   25. 3   26. 5
27. 3
28. Answers vary. Sample answer: For each row of the tables, I multiplied the number of people per household by the number of households. Then I added the products together and divided by the total number of households.

Practice Set 54

1. a. $\frac{3}{8}$ b. $\frac{3}{8}$
2. $2\frac{1}{8}$ inches
3. $8 * 12 = 96$; $12 * 8 = 96$; $\frac{96}{8} = 12$; $\frac{96}{12} = 8$
4. $9 * 5 = 45$; $5 * 9 = 45$; $\frac{45}{9} = 5$; $\frac{45}{5} = 9$
5. $7 * 9 = 63$; $9 * 7 = 63$; $\frac{63}{7} = 9$; $\frac{63}{9} = 7$
6. $8 * 11 = 88$; $11 * 8 = 88$; $\frac{88}{8} = 11$; $\frac{88}{11} = 8$
7. 384   8. 56   9. 1,302
10. 6   11. 27   12. 21
13. 107   14. 1,294   15. 1,044
16. 62   17. 4,503   18. 13,543
19. 144 plants   20. 8 gallons   21. $42
22. +5 pounds; 92 pounds

Practice Set 55

1. D   2. C   3. A   4. B
5. yes   6. no   7. yes   8. no
9. no   10. yes   11. yes   12. no
13. $6.00   14. 3   15. 15.5   16. 0.60
17. 6,000   18. 6.6   19. 2   20. 360
21. No; Answers vary. Sample answer: Multiplying the numerator and denominator by the same number will result in an equivalent fraction. Adding the same number to the numerator and denominator will increase the fraction by 1.
22. Rule: ÷ 2;
    $40,000 \rightarrow$ **20,000** $\rightarrow$ **10,000** $\rightarrow 5,000$
23. $30 \rightarrow$ **300** $\rightarrow$ **3,000** $\rightarrow$ **2,900** $\rightarrow$ **29,000** $\rightarrow$
    290,000 $\rightarrow$ **2,900,000** $\rightarrow$ **29,000,000**
24.

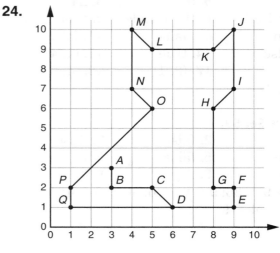

Practice Sets Answer Key *continued*

Practice Set 56

1. 0.2   **2.** 0.74   **3.** 0.3   **4.** 0.98
5. 0.4   **6.** 0.8   **7.** 0.39   **8.** 0.19
9. 0.7   **10.** 0.55   **11.** 0.4   **12.** 0.81
13. $18 \rightarrow$ **33**, $34 \rightarrow$ **49**, $41 \rightarrow 56$, $48 \rightarrow$ **63**,
    $90 \rightarrow$ **105**
14. $43 \rightarrow$ **21**, $34 \rightarrow$ **12**, $31 \rightarrow 9$, $18 \rightarrow$ **−4**,
    $99 \rightarrow 77$
15. $0 \rightarrow$ **0**, $2 \rightarrow 8$, $4 \rightarrow$ **16**, $10 \rightarrow$ **40**, $15 \rightarrow$ **60**
16. $18 \rightarrow$ **6**, $36 \rightarrow 12$, $60 \rightarrow$ **20**, $90 \rightarrow$ **30**,
    120 $\rightarrow 40$
17. $\frac{6}{6} = 1$ **18.** $\frac{5}{6}$ **19.** $\frac{5}{4} = 1\frac{1}{4}$ **20.** $\frac{3}{4}$

Practice Set 57

1. $<$ **2.** $<$ **3.** $>$ **4.** $=$
5. $>$ **6.** $=$ **7.** $=$ **8.** $>$
9. equal to $\frac{1}{2}$ **10.** less than $\frac{1}{2}$
11. greater than $\frac{1}{2}$ **12.** equal to $\frac{1}{2}$
13. greater than $\frac{1}{2}$ **14.** less than $\frac{1}{2}$
15. greater than $\frac{1}{2}$ **16.** less than $\frac{1}{2}$
17. 780,645   **18.** 201   **19.** 172
20. 4,880   **21.** 539   **22.** 84
23. 119   **24.** 565   **25.** 290
26. 533   **27.** 11,672   **28.** 1,801
29. 180   **30.** 7:10 A.M.   **31.** 3
32. 21   **33.** 4   **34.** 5
35. 3   **36.** 36   **37.** 8
38. 9   **39.** 60   **40.** 6

Practice Set 58

1. 18   **2.** 12   **3.** 35
4. 45   **5.** 9   **6.** 24
7. hundreds   **8.** thousands   **9.** thousands
10. tens   **11.** false   **12.** false
13. false   **14.** true   **15.** (1, 4)
16. (5, 2)   **17.** (3, 1)   **18.** (4, 5)
19. (2, 3)

Practice Set 59

1. true   **2.** false   **3.** false
4. true   **5.** false   **6.** 0
7. 1   **8.** 2   **9.** 7
10. $4 * 9 = 36; 9 * 4 = 36; 36 \div 9 = 4;$
    $36 \div 4 = 9$

11. $6 * 8 = 48; 8 * 6 = 48; 48 \div 6 = 8;$
    $48 \div 8 = 6$
12. $10 * 7 = 70; 7 * 10 = 70; 70 \div 7 = 10;$
    $70 \div 10 = 7$
13. $7 * 6 = 42; 6 * 7 = 42; 42 \div 7 = 6;$
    $42 \div 6 = 7$
14. 65   **15.** 96   **16.** 23
17. 8   **18.** 81   **19.** 90

Practice Set 60

1. 18 feet   **2.** 22 feet 10 inches
3. 14 feet   **4.** 78 feet   **5.** 16 km   **6.** 24 km
7. 80 km   **8.** 4 km   **9.** 20 km   **10.** 68 km
11. 110.41; 14,001; 41,000; 114,000
12. 4, 8, 16, **32, 64, 128**
13. 85, 90, 95, **100, 105, 110**
14. 16, 12, 8, **4, 0, −4**
15. 2, 0, −2, **−4, −6, −8**
16. 0.5 or 0.50   **17.** 0.77
18. 0.48   **19.** 0.09   **20.** 0.25   **21.** 0.5

Practice Set 61

1. 44 feet   **2.** 16 inches   **3.** 40 miles
4. 10 miles   **5.** 100 miles   **6.** 210 miles
7. 165 miles   **8.** 320 miles   **9.** 192
10. 304   **11.** 7,023   **12.** 30,000
13. 1,138   **14.** 106   **15.** 79   **16.** 44
17. 34   **18.** 51   **19.** 15   **20.** 133

Practice Set 62

1. 12 square units   **2.** 8 square units
3. 6 square units   **4.** 8 square units
5. 3   **6.** 18   **7.** 15   **8.** 11
9. 9   **10.** 8.5   **11.** 54   **12.** 16
13. 20   **14.** 32   **15.** 24   **16.** 56
17. 7   **18.** 35   **19.** 2   **20.** 12
21. 5   **22.** 4   **23.** 10   **24.** 72
25. 18   **26.** 32   **27.** 6   **28.** 45
29. 14   **30.** 12   **31.** 9   **32.** 48
33. 36   **34.** 12   **35.** 18   **36.** 21
37. 81   **38.** 7   **39.** 9   **40.** 9
41. 3   **42.** 49   **43.** 6   **44.** 8
45. 4   **46.** 45   **47.** 28   **48.** 4
49. 6   **50.** 8   **51.** 63   **52.** 32
53. 45   **54.** 8   **55.** 8

Practice Sets Answer Key *continued*

Practice Set 63

1. 22 feet; 14 feet
2. 128 square feet
3. 48 square feet
4. 132 square feet
5. Answers vary. Sample answer: I added 16 feet and 6 feet to find that the garden is 22 feet long. I multiplied 22 by the width of the flower section, which is 6 feet.
6. $(7 * 9) - 4 = 59$
7. $19 = 7 + (4 * 3)$
8. $(31 - 14) - 5 = 12$
9. $55 - (12 + 9) = 34$
10. $(4 * 9) + (4 * 12) = 84$
11. $44 = 4 * (7 + 4)$
12. $6 * (9 - 3) = 36$
13. $66 = (2 + 4) * (7 + 4)$
14. 36, 33, 30, **27, 24, 21**
15. 10, 25, 40, **55, 70, 85**
16. 48, 42, 36, **30, 24, 18**
17. 140, 125, 110, **95, 80, 65**
18. 32,000; 23,000; 3,200; 2,300
19. 4,900
20. 180
21. 900
22. 810
23. 10
24. 2,400
25. 8,000
26. 2
27. 20
28. 100
29. 1,600
30. 50
31. $\frac{8}{12}$ or $\frac{2}{3}$
32. $\frac{4}{12}$ or $\frac{1}{3}$
33. $\frac{6}{12}$ or $\frac{1}{2}$
34. $\frac{3}{12}$ or $\frac{1}{4}$
35. $1.80
36. $3.25
37. $1.75
38. $5.60
39. $12.40

Practice Set 64

1. 21 square inches
2. 4.2 square meters
3. $(115 - 63) + 25 = 77$
4. $158 - (18 + 32) = 108$
5. $(150 - 116) + 19 = 53$
6. $210 - (58 + 42) = 110$
7. 12
8. 24
9. 16,000
10. 7,500
11. 10,500
12. 99,000
13. about 8 cm

Practice Set 65

1. 20 square feet
2. 13.23 square feet
3. 12 meter
4. 20 feet
5. 3:18
6. 4:08
7. 5:26
8. 12:53
9. $\frac{53}{63}$
10. $\frac{13}{15}$
11. $\frac{23}{88}$
12. $\frac{13}{60}$
13. 5,363
14. 3,163
15. 104
16. 315
17. 20,000
18. 9.14
19. 9.5
20. 4.57
21. 108
22. 36
23. 1,154
24. 4,192
25.

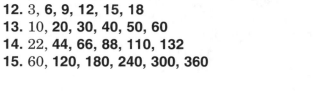

Practice Set 66

	Cities of Texas				
	City	Area	Area (rounded to nearest 100)	Estimate the number of times it would fit in the area of Anchorage	Divide the rounded areas. (Anchorage area ÷ city area)
1.	Houston	579 mi²	**600** mi²	2	1,697 ÷ **600** = **2.8** times
2.	Dallas	343 mi²	**300** mi²	5	1,697 ÷ **300** = **5.7** times
3.	Fort Worth	293 mi²	**300** mi²	5	1,697 ÷ **300** = **5.7** times
4.	Lubbock	115 mi²	**100** mi²	17	1,697 ÷ **100** = **17** times
5.	Waco	84 mi²	**100** mi²	17	1,697 ÷ **100** = **17** times

6. 240
7. 250
8. 180
9. 1,200
10. 70
11. 3,200
12. 3, **6, 9, 12, 15, 18**
13. 10, **20, 30, 40, 50, 60**
14. 22, **44, 66, 88, 110, 132**
15. 60, **120, 180, 240, 300, 360**

Practice Sets Answer Key *continued*

Practice Set 67

1. $\frac{23}{100}$, 23% **2.** $\frac{52}{100}$, 52%

3. $\frac{7}{100}$, 7% **4.** $\frac{10}{100}$, 10%

5. $\frac{80}{100}$, 0.80 **6.** $\frac{15}{100}$, 0.15

7. $\frac{1}{100}$, 0.01 **8.** $\frac{24}{100}$, 0.24

9. 0.83, $\frac{83}{100}$, 83% **10.** 0.40, $\frac{40}{100}$, 40%

11–18. Answers vary. Sample answers given.

11. $\frac{2}{12}$, $\frac{3}{18}$ **12.** $\frac{6}{14}$, $\frac{9}{21}$ **13.** $\frac{1}{3}$, $\frac{6}{18}$

14. $\frac{3}{4}$, $\frac{12}{16}$ **15.** $\frac{22}{28}$, $\frac{33}{42}$ **16.** $\frac{6}{10}$, $\frac{9}{15}$

17. $\frac{2}{2}$, $\frac{3}{3}$ **18.** $\frac{6}{10}$, $\frac{18}{30}$

19. 9 **20.** 5 **21.** 5 **22.** 9
23. 8 **24.** 4 **25.** 8 **26.** 6
27. 9 **28.** 7 **29.** 7 **30.** 9
31. 7 **32.** 3 **33.** 4 **34.** 4
35. 7 **36.** 0 **37.** 9 **38.** 9
39. 8 **40.** 6 **41.** 8 **42.** 4
43. 11 **44.** 7 **45.** 4 **46.** 7
47. 9 **48.** 4 **49.** 3 **50.** 5
51. 3 **52.** 8 **53.** 7 **54.** 6
55. 8 **56.** 6 **57.** 6 **58.** 8
59. 5 **60.** 10 **61.** 9 **62.** 9
63. 6

Practice Set 68

1. C **2.** G **3.** A **4.** F
5. H **6.** D **7.** E **8.** B
9. 15 → **300** → **6,000** → **120,000** → **2,400,000**
10. 0 → 200 → **400** → **600** → **800** → **1,000** →
 1,200 → **1,400** → **1,600**
11. Rule: −25; 718 → 693 → **668** → **643** → 618
 → **593** → **568**

Practice Set 69

1. a. 10 **b.** 10 **c.** 10
2. a. 5 **b.** 5 **c.** 5
3. $s = 5$ **4.** $t = 37$ **5.** $r = 42$
6. $n = 47$ **7.** $t = 130$ **8.** $y = 345$
9. $b = 800$ **10.** $c = 269$ **11.** 75,432
12. 76,332 **13.** 66,432 **14.** 76,422
15. 964,432,210
16. B **17.** D **18.** C
19. A **20.** 0.18 m **21.** 300 cm
22. 420 mm **23.** 45 cm **24.** 150 cm

25. 80 mm **26.** 10 cm **27.** 2 m
28. 0.75 m **29.** 1,550 mm

Practice Set 70

1. 0.91 **2.** 0.20 **3.** 0.35 **4.** 0.36
5. 0.30 **6.** 0.60 **7.** 70% **8.** 40%
9. 12.5% **10.** 30% **11.** 25% **12.** 37.5%
13. eighty **14.** eighty thousand
15. eighty thousand **16.** eight million
17. eight **18.** eight thousand
19. 74,009,064 **20.** 19.68
21. 409.827
22. seven hundred sixty-three thousandths
23. eighteen and four hundredths
24. octagon
25. 8 sides
26. 12 centimeters
27. Answers vary. Sample answer: I multiplied
 the length of one side, 1.5 cm, by the
 number of sides, 8.
28. 9 → **47**; 12 → **50**; 15 → **53**; 25 → **63**;
 100 → **138**
29. Rule: **out = in ∗ 70 or in = out ÷ 70**;
 6 → **420**; **11** → **770**
30. 80 → **−28**; 160 → **52**; 198 → 90; 2,400 →
 2,292; **1,308** → 1,200
31. Rule: **out = in ÷ 40 or in = out ∗ 40**;
 600 → **15**; 800 → **20**
32. 2 hours and 20 minutes
33. 2 days and 15 hours

Practice Set 71

1. 43% **2.** 7% **3.** 11% **4.** 15%
5. 9% **6.** 10% **7.** 6%
8. Answers vary. Sample answer: I divided the
 amount budgeted for each item by the total
 budget. I rounded the quotient to 2 digits and
 wrote the percent.
9. $11 **10.** 8 **11.** 1.9 **12.** 70¢
13. 72,000 **14.** 21.6 **15.** 70 **16.** 720
17. 175 **18.** 50

Practice Set 72

1. C **2.** A **3.** D **4.** E **5.** B
6. $\frac{1}{12}$, $\frac{1}{9}$, $\frac{1}{4}$, $\frac{1}{3}$, $\frac{1}{2}$ **7.** $\frac{4}{100}$, $\frac{4}{15}$, $\frac{4}{9}$, $\frac{4}{8}$, $\frac{4}{6}$
8. $\frac{1}{16}$, $\frac{3}{16}$, $\frac{5}{16}$, $\frac{7}{16}$, $\frac{15}{16}$

Practice Sets Answer Key *continued*

Practice Set 72 (cont.)

9. $1.09   **10.** 75¢   **11.** 34¢   **12.** 98¢
13. 95¢   **14.** 10¢   **15.** 25¢   **16.** 20¢
17. 20¢   **18.** 30¢   **19.** 60¢   **20.** 21.38
21. 12.53   **22.** 47.91   **23.** 9.57   **24.** 8.7
25. 12.37   **26.** 5.18   **27.** 47.72   **28.** 52.93
29. 10.93   **30.** $1.25   **31.** $3.22   **32.** $10.15
33. $229.25

Practice Set 73

1. 16.1   **2.** 37.8   **3.** 393.4   **4.** 15.3
5. 246.4   **6.** 17,532.0 **7.** 249.6   **8.** 21.93
9. 32.52   **10.** 104.4   **11.** 111.6   **12.** 85.28
13. 400   **14.** 20,000 **15.** 90   **16.** 0
17. $20 * 7 = 140$; 158.4
18. $6 * 8 = 48$; 50.4
19. $0.3 * 60 = 18$; 19.80
20. $10 * 40 = 400$; 508.0
21. true   **22.** false   **23.** false   **24.** true
25. $\frac{3}{12}$ or $\frac{1}{4}$ **26.** $\frac{3}{12}$ or $\frac{1}{4}$ **27.** $\frac{6}{12}$ or $\frac{1}{2}$
28. 78¢   **29.** 58¢   **30.** 76.964

Practice Set 74

1. 7.1   **2.** 0.21   **3.** 23.5
4. 11.4   **5.** 1.6   **6.** 7.3
7. about 3 inches
8.

```
          ┌──────────┐
          │ 78 + 22  │
          └──────────┘
               ▲
┌──────────┐ ┌─────┐ ┌──────────┐
│ 53 + 47  │◀│ 100 │▶│ 17 + 83  │
└──────────┘ └─────┘ └──────────┘
               ▼
          ┌──────────┐
          │ 49 + 51  │
          └──────────┘
```

9. 16, 36, 100
10. 0   **11.** 1   **12.** 1   **13.** 2

Practice Set 75

1. 11   **2.** 2   **3.** 9
4. 6   **5.** 6   **6.** 6
7. 3, **18, 33,** 48, **63, 78,** 93
8. 6, **16, 26, 36, 46,** 56
9. 11, **18, 25, 32, 39, 46,** 53
10. 14, **22, 30, 38,** 46, **54,** 62
11. 7 centimeters   **12.** 5 centimeters
13. 78,879   **14.** 17,372
15. 51,152   **16.** 48,446

Practice Set 76

1. no   **2.** yes   **3.** 200 mm
4. 5 m   **5.** 2,000 cm   **6.** 2,000 mm
7. 1,500 cm   **8.** 200 cm   **9.** 30.6 cm
10. 0.306 m   **11.** 60   **12.** 120
13. impossible; Answers vary. Sample answer: There are no green spaces on the spinner.

Practice Set 77

1. no   **2.** yes
3. 300,079,000   **4.** 4,065,700,000
5. 84,196,040,000   **6.** acute
7. straight   **8.** reflex   **9.** obtuse
10. $24 - 8 = 16$; true
11. $6 = 2 * 12$; false
12. $834 > 654$; true
13. $86 \div 2 = 43$; true
14. $98 - 16 = 84$; false
15. $27 > 8 + 15$; true
16. 16 square units; $2 * 8 = 16$
17. 15 square units; $5 * 3 = 15$
18. $0.23

Practice Set 78

1. yes   **2.** yes   **3.** no
4. no   **5.** yes   **6.** yes
7. $9 * (12 - 3) = 81$
8. $(9 * 12) - 3 = 105$
9. $15.8 = (2 * 6.5) + 2.8$
10. $18.6 = 2 * (6.5 + 2.8)$
11. $(7 * 1.1) + (4.2 * 12) = 58.1$
12. $(5 * 12) + (2 - 4) = 58$
13. $5 * (12 + 2) - 4 = 66$
14. $8,140 = 110 * (50 + 24)$
15. 48 in.   **16.** 9 ft   **17.** 41 in.
18. 7 ft   **19.** 3 ft 2 in.   **20.** 3 yd

Practice Set 79

1. 0.1   **2.** 0.5   **3.** 0.375   **4.** 0.6
5. 0.5   **6.** 0.47   **7.** 0.875   **8.** 0.75
9. 0.5625   **10.** 0.34   **11.** 0.56   **12.** 1.0
13. $2.18   **14.** 35¢   **15.** $1.83   **16.** $1.17
17. $1.23
18. 8, **12,** 16, **20,** 24, **28,** 32, **36,** 40, **44,** 48
19. 0, **18, 36,** 54
20. 0, **20, 40, 60, 80, 100, 120, 140, 160, 180, 200**

Practice Sets Answer Key *continued*

Practice Set 79 (cont.)

21. 6, **12**, **18**, 24

22. 18

23. $\frac{6}{18}$ or $\frac{1}{3}$

24. $\frac{8}{18}$ or $\frac{4}{9}$

25. $\frac{0}{18}$ or 0

26. Answers vary. Sample answer: There are no lemons in the picture, so the fraction of fruit that are lemons is $\frac{0}{18}$.

27. 900

28. 2

29. 765

30. 8

31. 53

32. 202

33. 26

34. 100

35. 1,063

36. 5

37. 0

38. 400

Practice Set 80

1. about 17°C

2. 180°F

3. 32°F; 18°C

4. 117°F

5. 60°C

6. −32°F

7. 48°C

8. bike riding

9. −15, −10, −5, **0, 5, 10**

10. 0.04. 0.06, 0.08, **0.1, 0.12, 0.14**

11. 0.44, 0.68, 0.92, **1.16, 1.4, 1.64**

12. 13 bags

13. 2 pieces

14. 15 bags

15. −4

16. −7

17. −1

18. 6

19. 1

20. 7

21. 7

22. −8

23. −8

24. Answers vary. Sample answer: I started at −6. I moved my pencil 7 numbers to the right. I ended at 1.

Practice Set 81

1. D

2. E

3. B

4. A

5. C

6. 20 paper clips

7. 2,000 paper clips

8. 60 paper clips

9. 960 paper clips

10. about 515 grams

11. 72

12. 12

13. 5

14. 84

15. 66

16. 45

17. 24

18. 8

19. 110

20. 77

Millions	Hundred-Thousands	Ten-Thousands	Thousands	Hundreds	Tens	Ones
1,000,000	100,000	10,000	1,000	100	10	1
10 [100,000s]	10 [10,000s]	10 [1,000s]	10 [100s]	10 [10s]	10 [1s]	10 [0.1s]
10∗10∗10∗ 10∗10∗10	10∗10∗10∗ 10∗10	10∗10∗ 10∗10	10∗10∗10	10∗10	10	
10^6	10^5	10^4	10^3	10^2	10^1	10^0

22. 110.4

23. 1.25

24. 20.13

25. 64.48

26. 91

27. 1,949.4

28. Answers vary. Sample answer: I know the figures are an example of a translation because they are the exact same size, shape, and orientation, but the second figure is moved over.

Practice Set 82

1. B

2. D

3. A

4. C

5. 4¢

6. 24¢

7. 8¢

8. 30¢

9. 44¢

10. 18¢

11. 45¢

12. 44¢

13. 67¢

14. 94¢

15. No; Answers vary. Sample answer: $1.69 ∗ 3 = $5.07. Joel needs 7¢ more to buy 3 pens.

Practice Set 83

1.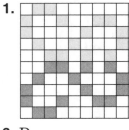

2.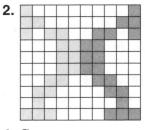

3. D

4. C

5. Answers vary. Sample answer: A cylinder is not made up of polygons, and it has curved sides.

6. <

7. >

8. <

9. <

10. >

11. >

Practice Set 84

1. 49 in.^{2}

2. 10.24 m^2

3. 135.8 cm^2

4. 135 ft^2

5. 154

6. 86

7. 28

8. 11

9. 1,223

10. 785

11. 9,100

12. 11,503

13. 4,150

14. 800

15. 99

16. 848

17. 170

18. 8

19. 1

20. 12

21. 444

22. 7

23. 17

24. 22

25. 5

26. 6

27. 108

28. 2

29. 8

30. 11

31. 9

32. 320

33. 12

34. 132

35. 25

36. 24

37. 40

38. 44

39. 33

40. 21

41. 28

42. 22

43. 9

44. 9

45. 110

46. 4

47. 9

48. 12

49. 11

50. 110

51. 81

52. 12

53. 56

54. 280

55. 12

56. 18

57. 60

58. 42

59. 81

60. 1,100

61. 4

62. 4

Practice Sets Answer Key *continued*

Practice Set 85

1. 54 cubic units   **2.** 30 cubic units
3. 36 cubic units   **4.** 64 cubic units

5–16. Answers vary. Sample answers given.

5. $\frac{2}{6}, \frac{8}{24}$ **6.** $\frac{9}{12}, \frac{30}{40}$ **7.** $\frac{1}{2}, \frac{4}{8}$

8. $\frac{10}{24}, \frac{25}{60}$ **9.** $\frac{5}{8}, \frac{20}{32}$ **10.** $\frac{2}{1}, \frac{28}{14}$

11. $\frac{1}{1}, \frac{8}{8}$ **12.** $\frac{12}{18}, \frac{2}{3}$ **13.** $\frac{6}{2}, \frac{9}{3}$

14. $\frac{6}{1}, \frac{12}{2}$ **15.** $\frac{0}{12}, \frac{0}{100}$ **16.** $\frac{4}{4}, \frac{10}{10}$

17. $\frac{7}{12}$ **18.** $\frac{3}{12}$ or $\frac{1}{4}$ **19.** $\frac{2}{12}$ or $\frac{1}{6}$

20. 30   **21.** 90   **22.** 80
23. 80   **24.** 12   **25.** 70
26. 60   **27.** 120
28. $9.30 or about $9.00
29. $35.88 or about $36.00
30. $4.05 or about $4.00
31. $59.97 or about $60.00
32. $33.96 or about $34.00

Practice Set 86

1. 16   **2.** 4   **3.** 0   **4.** 19
5. 4   **6.** 23   **7.** −25   **8.** −30
9. −7, −1.5, −0.2, $\frac{4}{9}$, 2.3, 8.3
10. −11, −5.5, −$\frac{8}{10}$, 1.85, $3\frac{2}{5}$, 4
11. −4, −3.7, 1.07, $\frac{17}{10}$, 9.09, 9.9

12. 90   **13.** 20,000   **14.** 80   **15.** 6,000
16. 40   **17.** 300   **18.** 8   **19.** 20
20. 175   **21.** 1,800   **22.** 6   **23.** 13,200
24. 25%   **25.** 75%   **26.** 100%   **27.** 57%
28. 15%   **29.** 40%   **30.** 40%   **31.** 37.5%
32. 80%   **33.** 112.5%   **34.** 76.5%   **35.** 40%
36. 200,000 cm   **37.** 25 m
38. 1.8 km   **39.** 30,000 m
40. 33 mm   **41.** 6,700 mm
42. 90°   **43.** 130°
44. 180°   **45.** 45°

Practice Set 87

1. 2 pints   **2.** 12 cups   **3.** 2 gallons
4. 5 pints   **5.** 6 cups   **6.** 14 quarts
7. 4:40   **8.** 5:15   **9.** 6:08
10. 7   **11.** 20   **12.** 9
13. 32   **14.** 6   **15.** 33

16. 40   **17.** 90   **18.** 330
19. 24   **20.** 3   **21.** 3
22. 933,167   **23.** 934,067   **24.** 924,167
25. 934,157   **26.** 1,076
27. 6,035   **28.** 960

Practice Set 88

1. $\frac{1}{10}, \frac{2}{10}, \frac{3}{10}, \frac{4}{10}, \frac{5}{10}, \frac{6}{10}, \frac{7}{10}, \frac{8}{10}$
2. 3.5, 3.8, 4.1, **4.4, 4.7,** 5.0, **5.3,** 5.6
3. 12, **14,** 16, 18, **20, 22, 24,** 26
4. **−72,** −60, −48, **−36,** −24, **−12, 0, 12**
5. 2, 2.75, **3.5,** 4.25, **5,** 5.75, 6.5, **7.25**
6. 13, **20, 27, 34, 41, 48, 55,** 62
7. −32°C   **8.** −13°C
9. 15 cookies   **10.** 3 cookies

Practice Set 89

1. 150 miles   **2.** 5 gallons

gallons	*100*	200	300	400	500	600	700
day	1	2	3	4	5	6	7

3. 700 gallons   **4.** 36,400 gallons

dresses	*3*	6	9	12	15	18
hours	2	4	6	8	10	12

5. 12 dresses   **6.** 10 or 11 dresses
7. =   **8.** =   **9.** <
10. >   **11.** >   **12.** >
13. 17   **14.** 15   **15.** 15
16. 360   **17.** 0.2   **18.** 7.7
19. 1   **20.** 660   **21.** 33
22. 405   **23.** 30   **24.** 93
25. $a = 24$ **26.** $b = 4$ **27.** $c = 4$
28. $d = 111$ **29.** $e = 3$ **30.** $f = 10,830$
31. $g = 7$ **32.** $h = 160$ **33.** 10,000
34. 5   **35.** 2   **36.** 4
37. 100,000,000   **38.** 3,000,000
39. third   **40.** 1

Practice Set 90

minutes	3	6	9	12	15	18
pages	1	2	3	4	5	6

1. 5 pages   **2.** 10 pages

miles	55	110	165	220	275	330
hours	1	2	3	4	5	6

3. 275 miles   **4.** about $5\frac{1}{2}$ hours

papers	14	28	42	56	70	84
minutes	1	2	3	4	5	6

5. 84 papers   **6.** 50 minutes

price	$1.30	$2.60	$3.90	$5.20	$6.50	$7.80
pounds	1	2	3	4	5	6

7. $6.50
8. a little less than 8 pounds
9. 0.08   **10.** 0.6   **11.** 0.3
12. 0.33   **13.** 0.25   **14.** 0.47
15. 0.5   **16.** 0.25   **17.** 0.375
18. 0.42   **19.** 0.182   **20.** 0.778
21. 23, 610; 23, 615; 23, 620; **23,625; 23,630; 23,635**
22. 39.55; 39.50; 39.45; **39.40; 39.35; 39.30**
23. 151; 148; 145; **142; 139; 136**
24. 1,455; 1,130; 805; **480; 155; −170**
25. 100   **26.** 3
27. 6   **28.** 4
29. 36 cubic units   **30.** 24 cubic units

Practice Set 91

1. 26 miles   **2.** $0.68
3. $1.50 per card   **4.** 9 minutes per mile
5. $\frac{6}{18}$ or $\frac{1}{3}$ **6.** $\frac{6}{18}$ or $\frac{1}{3}$
7. $\frac{6}{18}$ or $\frac{1}{3}$ **8.** 96¢   **9.** 71¢

Practice Set 92

1. a. 25¢
  b. 30¢ per can; better buy: 4 cans of peaches for $1.00
2. a. 28¢

  b. 22¢ per ounce; better buy: 1 pound of raisins for $3.52
3. a. 25¢
  b. 20¢ per egg; better buy: 1 dozen eggs for $2.40
4. a. 35¢
  b. 35¢ per box; better buy: neither
5. >   **6.** =   **7.** <   **8.** >   **9.** >
10. $\frac{1}{10}, \frac{1}{4}, \frac{3}{6}, \frac{9}{12}, \frac{16}{16}$
11. true   **12.** false   **13.** false
14. true   **15.** 20   **16.** 12
17. 12   **18.** 90   **19.** true
20. false   **21.** true   **22.** false
23. false   **24.** false

Practice Set 93

1.

Tickets	60	120	180	240	300	360
Hours	1	2	3	4	5	6

6 hours

2.

Labels	120	240	360	480	600	720
Weeks	1	2	3	4	5	6

720 soup labels

3.

Miles	65	130	195	260	325	390
Hours	1	2	3	4	5	6

260 miles

4. 32.8   **5.** 8.4   **6.** 674.1
7. 18.0   **8.** 1.7   **9.** 1,905.4

Test Practice Correlated to Grade 4 Goals

Test Practice	Use with or after:	Problem	*Everyday Mathematics* Grade 4 Grade-Level Goals
1	Unit 3	1	Number and Numeration Goal 1
		2	Data and Chance Goal 2
		3	Data and Chance Goal 2
		4	Geometry Goal 2
		5	Operations and Computation Goal 3
		6	Geometry Goal 1
		7	Operations and Computation Goal 2
		8	Geometry Goal 2
2	Unit 6	1	Operations and Computation Goal 2
		2	Number and Numeration Goal 5
		3	Operations and Computation Goal 2
		4	Operations and Computation Goal 6
		5	Operations and Computation Goal 4
		6	Operations and Computation Goal 6
3	Unit 9	1	Data and Chance Goal 2
		2	Number and Numeration Goal 5
		3	Number and Numeration Goal 5
		4	Data and Chance Goal 4
		5	Data and Chance Goal 4
		6	Measurement and Reference Frames Goal 2
		7	Measurement and Reference Frames Goal 2
4	Unit 12	1	Measurement and Reference Frames Goal 4
		2	Geometry Goal 3
		3	Geometry Goal 3
		4	Operations and Computation Goal 3
		5	Patterns, Functions, and Algebra Goal 1
		6	Operations and Computation Goal 4
		7	Number and Numeration Goal 6
		8	Number and Numeration Goal 1
		9	Operations and Computation Goal 4

Test Practice Answer Key

Test Practice 1

1. B
2. C
3. A
4. C
5. A
6. A
7. B
8. A

Test Practice 2

1. B
2. D
3. D
4. B
5. B
6. B

Test Practice 3

1. D
2. D
3. A
4. D
5. B
6. A
7. C

Test Practice 4

1. B
2. D
3. B
4. B
5. C
6. C
7. C
8. D
9. B